MASS!

Robert Kennedy and Dennis B. Weis

CONTEMPORARY
BOOKS, INC.
CHICAGO ▪ NEW YORK

Published by Contemporary Books, Inc.
180 North Michigan Avenue, Chicago, Illinois 60601
Manufactured in the United States of America
International Standard Book Number: 0-8092-4940-5

Published simultaneously in Canada by Beaverbooks, Ltd.
195 Allstate Parkway, Valleywood Business Park
Markham, Ontario L3R 4T8 Canada

Dedicated to Donne Hale

CONTENTS

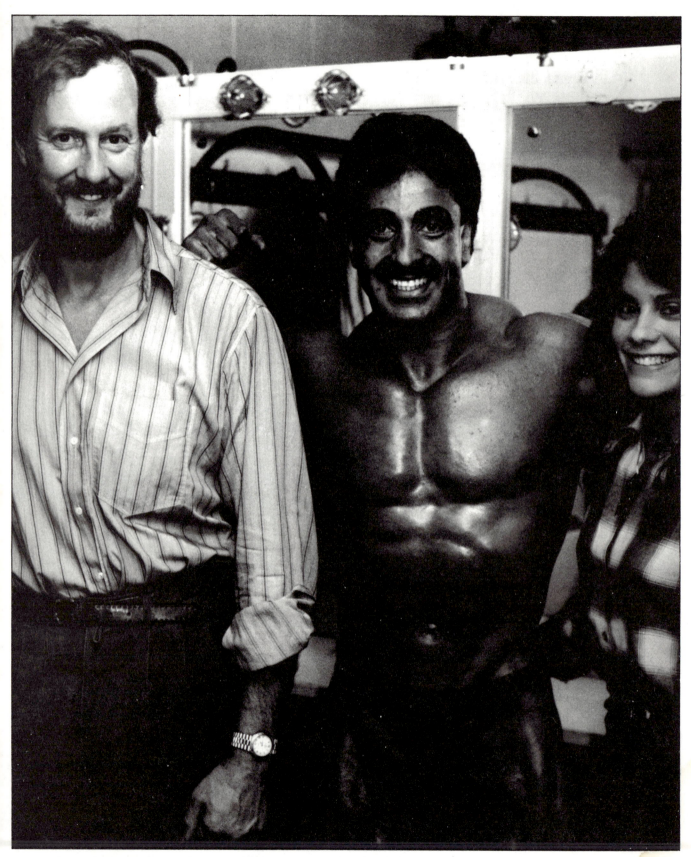

Author Robert Kennedy with Samir and Lori Bannout.

ABOUT THE AUTHORS

Robert Kennedy is well known to the bodybuilding world as the publisher of *MuscleMag International*, a monthly magazine for male and female bodybuilders that he started in 1974.

Like coauthor Dennis Weis, Kennedy has trained for many years and has competed successfully in both weightlifting and bodybuilding contests. He was born in England in 1938 and emigrated to Canada at the age of 30.

Kennedy has written dozens of books on bodybuilding, including best-sellers *Hardcore Bodybuilding*, *Beef It!*, *Pumping Up!* (coauthored with Ben Weider), and *Reps!* He was trained as an artist, specializing in oil painting and stone carving, and to this day he keeps up with both. He has had one-man art exhibitions in London, England; Salzburg, Austria; and Toronto, Canada.

His avid interest in bodybuilding, a sport he still practices today, has made him one of the most knowledgeable and respected people in the field.

Coauthor Dennis B. Weis is a former bodybuilding and physique champion and is now a feature writer and researcher for such worldwide bodybuilding journals as *Iron Man*, *MuscleMag International*, *Muscular Development*, and *Powerlifting USA*.

He was born in Everett, Washington, in 1945, but he has been a resident of Alaska for the greater part of his life.

His involvement in bodybuilding represents more than 24 years of painstaking research in which he has spent hundreds of hours going over exercise physiology studies, ultimately developing the most advanced bodybuilding programs ever known.

Along with his extensive research, he has found time to write scores of articles on many of the top names in bodybuilding: Boyer Coe, Jeff King, Bill Pearl, Larry Scott, Chuck Sipes, and Frank Zane, to name just a few.

Weis is a prolific writer who has written four of his own hard-hitting books on bodybuilding and super strength training, published by Iron Man Publishing Company in Alliance, Nebraska. His most recent work, *Special Advice to the Bodybuilder*, is fast becoming a best-seller.

Dennis is modest about his own accomplishments in the iron game, but his best lifetime lifts are nothing to be quiet about. He has squatted 75 reps with an amazing 300 pounds. Additionally, he has deadlifted 630 pounds, leg-pressed 800 pounds for 20 reps, and quarter-squatted with 1,000 pounds for 20 reps.

The main man of mass Lee Haney, 1984, 1985 Mr. Olympia winner.

ACKNOWLEDGMENTS

This book is not the result of our efforts exclusively. There are many people to thank.

Accordingly, grateful appreciation is heaped on photographers Steve Douglas, Garry Bartlett, Chris Lund, Roger Shelley, Doris Barrilleaux, Al Antuck, John Balik, Mike Neveaux, Reg Bradford, Wayne Gallasch, Paul Good, Bill Heimanson, Ken Korentayer, Glenn Low, Lance Mitchell, Lou Parees, Denie Walter, Bill Reynolds, Joe Valdez, André Cushing, Russ Warner, Eric Chapman, and Mike Read.

To Gold's and World's gyms, to Super Fitness and Golden Fitness, to Vince's and Fitness Plus, we say, Thanks a million for letting our staff in to photograph the champions.

From Weis: Perry Rader has been the cornerstone of my success. I owe him my sincere gratitude. And I would like to thank my beautiful wife Faith for her patience and help in this endeavor.

We would also like to acknowledge the work done by the IFBB, specifically Joe and Ben Weider. They all but created bodybuilding as it is known today, glamorized it through *Muscle and Fitness* and *Flex* magazines, and legitimized it as a sport through the international network of the IFBB. Without them, a wide market for this book would not exist.

Last but not least, we thank the champions themselves. Frequently they pose for photographers when they would rather rest, or they put up with flashing cameras while they are going for that last rep! In every instance, we appreciate their willingness and kind cooperation.

Tom Platz epitomizes massive muscularity. Here he shows his engorged bicep.

INTRODUCTION

For the advanced bodybuilder, *Mass!* has it all. If ever there was a scientific bodybuilding book, this is it! We don't mess around in this book. By combining 100-percent muscle talk with a bounty of photos of those stars you've come to admire, we've come up with a manual that offers a veritable wealth of up-to-date, exciting enlightenment.

Veteran Vince Gironda once said, "There are more gyms, books, magazines, and training courses on bodybuilding than ever before in history. Hardly a day goes by where we don't see the invention of a new 'progressive resistance' apparatus on the market, yet people are still in the dark. They crave one thing over everything else: bodybuilding know-how, good information."

Mass! starts where other books leave off. We both have a deep-rooted interest in getting to the very soul of bodybuilding knowledge. Be warned: *Mass!* is an *advanced* book. It is *not* for the beginner, not even for lukewarm intermediates. It is spe-cifically designed for the advanced man or woman who has trained seriously for at least a year. But if you really are prepared to *use* this book as it should be used, to work according to its suggestions, then the sky's the limit!

Needless to say, before you start any exercise program or diet you should check with your doctor. If you have a family history of heart disease, high serum cholesterol, circulatory deficiency, inflated blood pressure, or other organic problems, you should participate only with the approval and under the supervision of your family physician.

To the hale and hardy, we say, join us. Come on in and fight your way to the top of this magnificent sport.

Use this book to break out with new enthusiasm for your personal bodybuilding adventure. Let nothing stop you. If you have the will, *Mass!* will give you the way! Now, at last, you are in a position to "force-feed" your muscles to titanic new dimensions.

What does *Mass!* contain that you will not find in any other volume? Chances are that as you leaf through this book you will learn something new from almost every page. This is a book with a difference. There are extensive sections on muscle-building nutrition, phase training, muscle blasting, weight loss, speeding up the metabolism, strengthening the heart, structuring the workout routine—you name it!

We worked hard and long on the production of *Mass!* We took many of the pictures on location in Britain, Sweden, Canada, Poland, Belgium, and the U.S. Also, literally years have been spent in the formulation of the muscle charts that you see within these pages. (How much should you weigh? How big can you get? What should you be bench pressing? What is your body fat percentage?) All the diets

Sergio Oliva—"The Myth."

and blender muscle drinks have been painstakingly tested, as have the routines and other training suggestions. This book is *not* based on mere theory; rather, its contents have been arrived at through empirical discovery. Here we touch on the previously untouched. Indeed, *Mass!* has broached subjects like warm-ups, injuries, blitz nutrition, water retention, and intensity principles, which have hardly merited a mention in other books.

Mass! also has a chapter on carbing up during that final precontest week. We take you through every phase, step by step. There's a section detailing the seven-week weight-gaining blitz cycle, and we give you a strategy for beating the water retention problem. A special exercise selection chart will help you choose exactly the right movements for your muscle-building needs, plus a 15-day calf blitz program. We give extensive advice on reducing the waistline and developing abdominals that really show, plus an entire lesson in using the jettison muscle-building method.

This book contains the collective wisdom of the top pros in bodybuilding—more than mere sound advice and flamboyant ideas. There's dynamite in here: blitz techniques and diet advice to knock your socks off! *Mass!* has answers to questions you may not even have known enough to ask. And we will help you put muscles in places where you didn't even know you had muscles!

So far you have put some beef on your frame. Now let's take it a step further: make your next workout a brand-new step in the direction of *total* muscle success. Muscle building is your life. We know it. *You* know it. Let this volume be your training partner to lead you to the very peak of muscular achievement. We are with you; you need *Mass!* So let's get started!

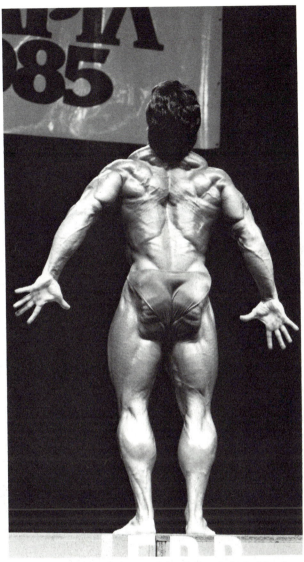

The ripped back of bodybuilding's brightest new star—Rich Gaspari.

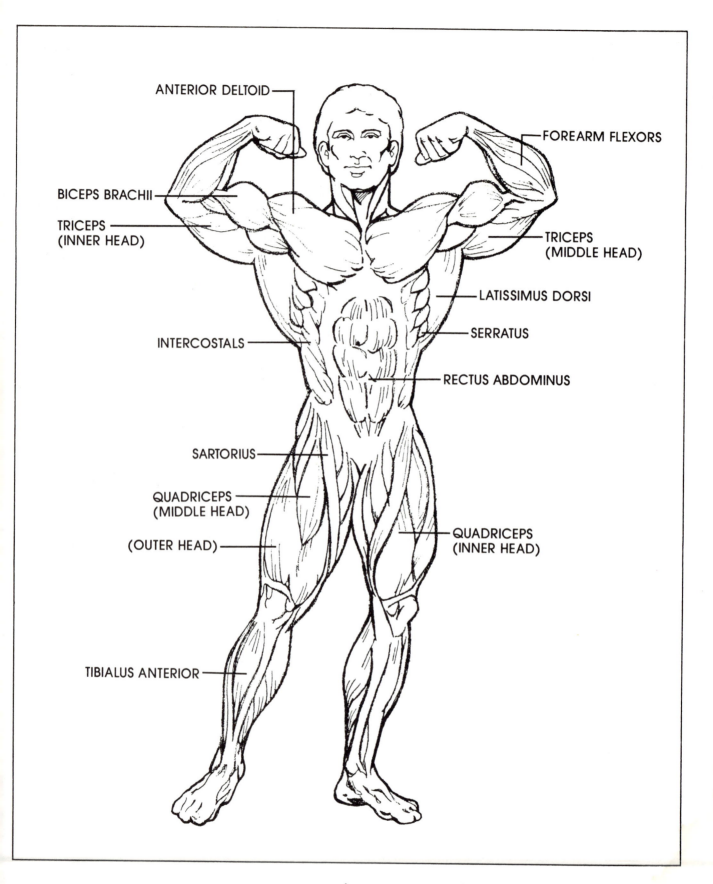

ANTERIOR DELTOID

FOREARM FLEXORS

BICEPS BRACHII

TRICEPS
(INNER HEAD)

TRICEPS
(MIDDLE HEAD)

LATISSIMUS DORSI

SERRATUS

INTERCOSTALS

RECTUS ABDOMINUS

SARTORIUS

QUADRICEPS
(MIDDLE HEAD)

QUADRICEPS
(INNER HEAD)

(OUTER HEAD)

TIBIALUS ANTERIOR

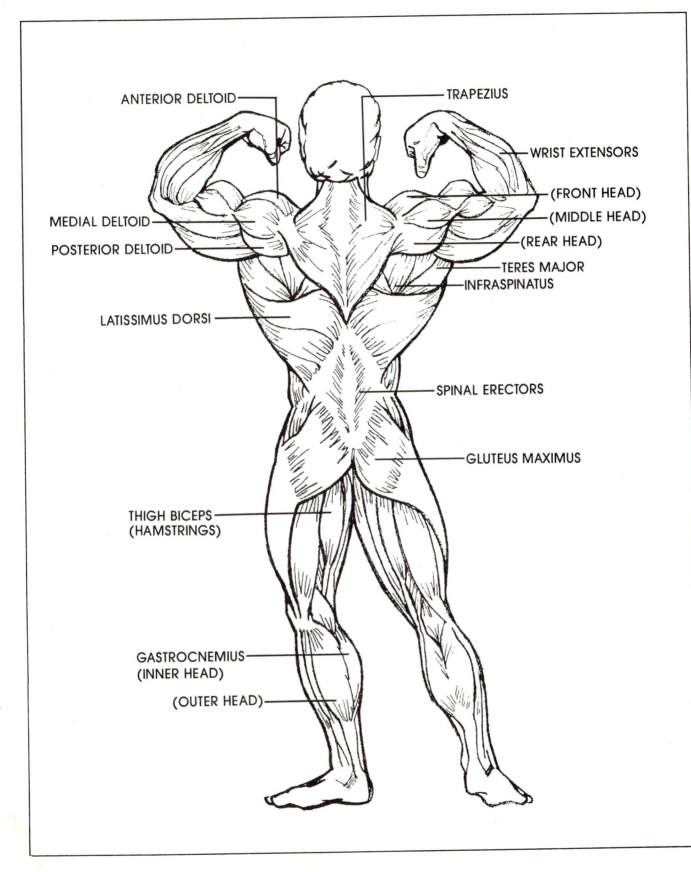

ANTERIOR DELTOID

TRAPEZIUS

WRIST EXTENSORS

(FRONT HEAD)

(MIDDLE HEAD)

MEDIAL DELTOID

(REAR HEAD)

POSTERIOR DELTOID

TERES MAJOR

INFRASPINATUS

LATISSIMUS DORSI

SPINAL ERECTORS

GLUTEUS MAXIMUS

THIGH BICEPS
(HAMSTRINGS)

GASTROCNEMIUS
(INNER HEAD)

(OUTER HEAD)

What an arm! Mike Christian uses visualization techniques to build his mountainous bicep.

1
CONCENTRATION—THE BODYBUILDER'S WAY

We feel it's appropriate to start a book on building muscle mass with a chapter on concentration. After many years in the sport, we have concluded that the mind is responsible for your rate of progress. Three-time Mr. Olympia winner Frank Zane has always emphasized that successful bodybuilding begins in the mind. So has Arnold Schwarzenegger.

Concentration is a key to the achievement of stunning bodybuilding progress and is one of the most important factors in the actual physical performance of a workout. It seems that no matter how diligently you apply yourself to the successful completion of the exercise you are doing, your mind will begin to wander to other things, such as academic, financial, and family problems; personality conflicts; and workout scheduling conflicts (due to lack of training time). Relentlessly, other intrusions from the mind interrupt your concentration capacity.

This is natural, but as you continue to push forward in your bid to succeed in bodybuilding, you will eventually reach a point where you will be able to shut out most of these intrusions.

The following seven steps will help you greatly in achieving super *shutout* concentration.

1. Always think about your training in a positive manner.
2. Block out all negative thoughts.
3. Plan your workouts so that you won't be interrupted.
4. Don't make an excuse to miss a workout.
5. Don't let your thoughts wander to other things; make every exercise movement mental as well as physical.
6. Always be pleasant to others, but make it clear that you are training and nothing must interfere with your workout.
7. The visual imagery technique: This is a type of focusing on the concentration link between the mind and the muscle.

It is a training secret that all of the top bodybuilding champions use to shock their muscles into new dimensions of growth.

EXPLORING THE VISUAL IMAGERY TECHNIQUE

The idea behind this technique is to form clear and vivid pictures in your mind of the perfect set of repetitions you plan on doing prior to actually performing the set.

Using the bench press, it goes something like this: sit on the edge of your exercise bench and close your eyes. Mentally (remembering to let clear and vivid pictures form in your mind) visualize yourself lying back on the bench, making sure that your shoulders and buttocks are

Raven Dosne concentrates on a bicep curl.

Rich Gaspari—mind over muscle.

in full contact with the bench. The small of the back is arched (helps shorten the distance that the barbell must travel and also kicks the lats in as a support muscle), and the feet are planted firmly on the floor.

Taking a hand spacing that will activate the most pressing muscle response for your body type, smoothly lift the barbell out off the upright supports (using a spotter will help you conserve valuable lifting energy).

Your arms are locked; now see yourself unlocking your powerful arms and begin lowering the barbell at a medium speed to the chest. Lowering the barbell too slowly will cause you to lose valuable energy, which is necessary later for pushing past the "sticking point." Inhale as you lower the bar to your chest.

Just as the barbell touches the chest

Kal Szkalak crunches out a barbell curl.

weight off the chest in an even and controlled manner.

After the initial blast off the chest, there often is a slight arm lag. To overcome this problem, focus your vision on the very center of the bar.

Continue to feel yourself becoming more and more powerful as you steadily apply more effort to pressing the barbell to the lockout position.

This completes the visualization of one *perfect* rep. Continue to rehearse this for each additional repetition you plan on performing in the particular set.

You will see no failure, only success with each repetition completed in a strong, positive way. You should now be mentally and physically ready to begin the actual physical set of repetitions.

You should use visual imagery in all areas of your muscle-building program, from warming up to cooling down. You won't find one successful bodybuilder today who doesn't utilize this principle to its fullest.

(this should be at a point that will bring the tips of your elbows to a position as close as possible to parallel to the floor), visualize yourself channeling all the strength of every muscle fiber involved in the movement. See those horseshoe-like triceps, armor-plated pecs, and coconut deltoids literally blast or explode the

Frank Richards pumps up backstage.

2
THE SCIENCE OF REPS AND SETS

WARMING UP

Muscles don't have brains; they will react as they're instructed. Therefore it is essential to warm up properly for safe and effective muscle-blasting routines.

It isn't enough to do only one or two general warm-up exercises (calisthenics, push-ups, running in place, etc.) at the beginning of your planned workout schedule. You should also warm up with the general and/or specific exercise that you will be doing for a particular body part. The secret to this is to warm up the muscles without fatiguing them to the point at which your productivity in the primary work sets is decreased.

A good warm-up procedure to follow is to perform one or two sets (resting for 30–60 seconds between these sets) per individual exercise, using two-thirds of the maximum repetition poundage you plan on using. For example, if you plan on

maxing out with 10 reps with 200 pounds in the lat pulldown behind the neck, you should use approximately 135 pounds for these two warm-up sets.

THE BENEFITS

1. Warm-ups help to reduce muscle injury. When a muscle hasn't been warmed up properly, it may tear or pull if it is suddenly required to contract against a maximum application of effort.
2. The muscle contracts more efficiently at warmer inner body temperatures.
3. Warm-ups increase the blood flow to the primary muscle being worked.
4. Increased blood flow means better range of the movement in the muscles and joints.
5. Warm-ups stimulate the nerve pathway to the muscle, which is very important to the muscle contraction.

6. Warm-ups increase the oxygen delivery to the muscles.

While doing one or two sets is the general practice for warm-ups, you must take into consideration the existing temperature in your training environment. Warm-up time will be longer if it is colder than usual. When you are working out in a commercial gym, this is not usually a problem, but many bodybuilders train in home gyms. Many of these gyms lack proper heating. During the summer you might be training in an 80-degree atmosphere, but in winter the temperature in your home gym might be 32 degrees. Always wear a warm-up suit during cold weather, because it will help to maintain body heat and keep the muscles tuned for the workout.

Now that you have warmed up, let's analyze the science of reps and sets.

The key to unlocking your potential in size and strength is the use of certain repetition and set schemes in your exercise program. As experienced bodybuilders, you're undoubtedly familiar with repetitions and sets, but you may not know how to use them to your greatest

Bill Grant pumps iron to his favorite music at Gold's Gym.

advantage. Before we get into specific techniques for making the most of reps and sets, let's review definitions of those terms.

Definition of Repetition

A repetition is basically the performance of the same exercise through its complete range of movement from beginning to end, over and over.

Example: Standing Two-Hand Barbell Curl   Grasp a barbell with hands about shoulder width apart, palms up. Begin by curling the barbell to its contracted position, which is generally under the chin. Slowly lower the barbell to the starting (stretched) position.

This is one repetition; immediately repeat the sequence, and you have done two repetitions.

Definition of Set

After you have repeated the above cycle for a number of repetitions and momentarily

Not many people perform chins this way, but Mohamed Makkawy does for super wide lats.

cannot do another one, you have completed a set.

Gladys Portugues performing heavy "hacks" under Mohamed Makkawy's supervision.

Example You have just completed eight repetitions in the standing two-hand barbell curl and have reached a point where you momentarily can't do another rep. You then put the barbell down on the floor and rest. This is one set of eight reps. After a short pause or rest, you begin the entire sequence once again. This represents two sets.

DEVISING A SCHEME OF REPS AND SETS

Reps and sets are dictated to a great extent by your physical and emotional needs. You've probably noticed this in reading various bodybuilding magazines. There seem to be as many different rep and set schemes as there are bodybuilding champions.

Another important factor in determining the number of reps and sets you might use is the individual characteristics of the muscle cell itself. These characteristics in part determine the stress that needs to be applied to the muscle.

Reps

Three major components make up a muscle cell: (1) The *myofibrils* contribute to 20–30 percent of the cell size. (2) The *mitochondria* contribute to 15–25 percent of the cell size. (3) The *sarcoplasm* contributes to 20–30 percent of the muscle cell size.

The remainder of each muscle cell is made up of capillaries, 3–5 percent; connective tissue, 2–3 percent; fat deposits, 10–15 percent; glycogen, 2–5 percent; and other subcellular substances, 4–7 percent.

The three major cellular components combined contribute 55–85 percent to cell size, so let's examine the primary function and capacity in a repetition scheme of each one.

Myofibrils The myofibrils are the components in a muscle cell that allow the muscle to sustain a maximum contraction for maximum power and strength. There are a couple of ways to stimulate the myofibrils to grow in number and strength.

First, for power, perform three to five reps with 88–92 percent of your current one-rep maximum. For example, if your best squat for one rep is 500 pounds, take 92 percent of 500, which equals 460 pounds. The reps should be done consecutively and as quickly (explosively) as possible through the complete range of the movement, without sacrificing your lifting form.

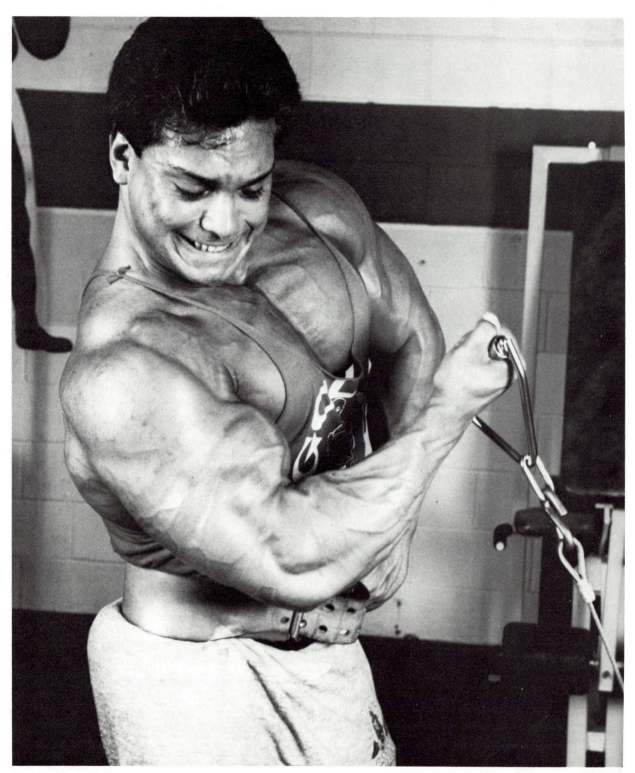

The "arm pumpout" by Rich Gaspari. This young champion pays particular attention to his scheme of reps and sets.

With this method it is possible to gain strength without much size. Why? Because a muscle requires a minimum of 36 seconds of continuous tension to activate much in the way of muscle size, and the three- to five-rep scheme does not always meet this demand.

However, this rep scheme is excellent for recruiting more nerve motor units to fire instantaneously in a given moment, and this results in a stronger muscle contraction.

This is the secret to why, in certain situations, a person of a slight build is able to lift more than a person who is 50 pounds heavier.

This repetition selection is generally used as part of a contest training cycle by powerlifters. The exercises that generally are used within this rep structure are the squat, bench press, and deadlift.

Second, for the best combination of size and strength in the myofibril element, do six to eight reps with 84–88 percent of your current one-rep maximum. The speed of the rep differs from the above in that it should be of medium cadence, where it takes two seconds to

Mike Christian pops a quick pose between sets.

move the weight up and four seconds to lower the weight.

Mitochondria When developed, the mitochondria increase the endurance quality of the muscle cell by bringing in more blood and oxygen into the muscle. Your rep scheme here should be a 15–25 count with about 60–78 percent of your current one-rep maximum. Your repetition speed should be the same as for the above-mentioned size and strength scheme. You can, however, experiment from time to time with an extremely slow rep speed, where you go to a 10-second-up/4-second-down time factor.

The 10-up-and-4-down rep speed will be a tremendous help to you in improving your exercise technique and eliminating excess body momentum.

Performing high reps may appear easy when you see it written down on paper, but be assured that as you begin to perform the reps the tension and fatigue you will experience in the muscle during the final two or three reps will be as hard as the tension fatigue experienced in the final rep or two of a strength-building set.

Mitochondria-building reps of 15–25 are beneficial in three ways:

Carla Dunlap performs a squat with an extra-wide stance.

Jusup Wilcosz of West Germany performs the incline barbell press.

1. They build overall aerobic fitness, if you are following a well-executed weight-training aerobic program such as circuit training or PHA weight training.

2. They increase your localized muscular endurance. What we are speaking of here is the endurance you achieve in a certain body part by performing specific exercises. For example, you will develop a degree of endurance in your biceps from performing the barbell curl for 15–25 reps. Likewise, many isolation movements (dumbbell lateral raises for the deltoids or dumbbell flyes for the outer pectoralis) will develop local endurance in those muscle areas when applying the above rep pattern, and very little endurance in other body parts will result from these specific lever movements.

The compound movements (exercises that involve two or more muscle groups) such as the squat will not only develop endurance in the legs but will also contribute some endurance to the lower back. Deadlifts not only develop the lower back but can create gains as well in localized muscular endurance in the traps and forearms.

Your recovery between workout ses-

Chris Dickerson shows Olympian symmetry.

sions is much faster than medium-volume/medium-intensity or low-volume/high-intensity workouts.

3. They promote rib cage expansion through the use of high-rep, deep-breathing squats alternated with lightweight, stiff-arm breathing pullovers.

If your high-rep training is done for a specific body part, it should always be performed as the last set or two of an exercise for that body part.

High reps produce very high lactic acid levels within the body, and when you fail at a certain rep it is generally due to cardiovascular fatigue rather than muscular fatigue (your muscles outrun your lungs). For example, at the conclusion of your squat workout, you take a weight that is 60–78 percent of your best single attempt in the squat. You will then do as many reps as possible with this weight until you just can't do any more (can't even raise up two inches). You will need a spotter or a safety squat rack for this procedure.

As your muscles begin to fatigue, you will have to resort to extreme mental tenacity to make the muscles contract. Remember: more muscle cells must be

Two-time Ms. Olympia Rachel McLish gives fullest contraction to her incline flyes.

brought into play in faster work shifts. Instead of giving up when it seems hopeless, do more and more! This trains your muscles to obey your will.

For a middle-of-the-road rep scheme that will develop muscle size (hypertrophy), muscle contractile force (myofibril strength), and a very slight degree of endurance (mitochondria), you will want to employ a rep pattern of 8–12 with 80 percent of your one-rep maximum.

Muscle hypertrophy, as you probably know, is the structural change in a muscle cell that allows the cell to increase in size.

You will experience two types of hypertrophy in your training. The first is

Mohamed Makkawy uses cable curls for peaking his biceps.

chronic hypertrophy, which is a lasting increase in the muscle cell structure and is permanent only as long as there is some type of direct stimulus to the muscle. The second type of hypertrophy is called *transitory.* It is that "pumped" feeling you notice in a muscle after it has been stimulated by a series of repetitions. This type of muscle hypertrophy is only temporary in nature and soon disappears after a workout.

Sarcoplasm   Sarcoplasm is a protein liquid substance that saturates and surrounds all of the components in a muscle cell. Sarcoplasm increases proportionately with the increases in myofibril and mitochondria.

The Wrap-Up on Reps   The myofibrils and the mitochondria make up the greatest percentage of a muscle's cell size. It is therefore obvious that you should divide your training equally between the two to be assured of developing both of these components to their maximum.

The contractile strength of a muscle cell is proportionate to the percentage of its myofibril content. Usually, a muscle that has a greater percentage of this component is classed as a *fast-twitch* muscle. Likewise, the endurance capacity of a

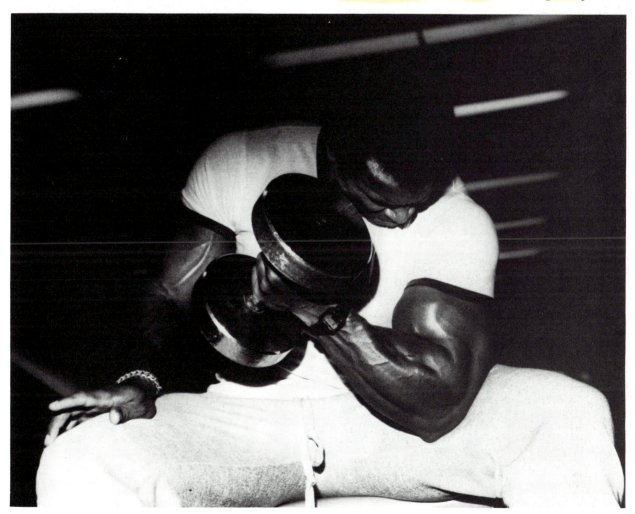

Frenchman Serge Nubret performs his favorite biceps exercise: the concentration curl.

Tom Platz—"The Golden Eagle."

muscle cell is generally proportionate to the mitochondria content and is thought of as a *slow-twitch* muscle.

The subject of *fast-* and *slow*-twitch muscle training deserves some discussion, simply because it is one of the most abused points in bodybuilding circles today. No muscle is completely fast or slow twitch, and everyone has a different percentage of these muscle fibers.

Obviously, if a bodybuilder has more of the slow-twitch (red) fibers, more than likely he or she will be capable of performing more reps in a particular set than, say, a bodybuilder who has predominately more fast-twitch (white) fibers. This individual is probably capable of performing a much higher maximum single repetition.

To the bodybuilder, the bottom line is to mix up your repetition patterns from time to time to ensure that you are developing the fast (white) and slow (red) muscle fibers to their maximum potential.

True and absolute strength gains will result after the initial six to eight weeks of training. Any gains in strength prior to this period result mostly from a learning process of the muscle, nerves, and mind working together as one unit.

Beginners to bodybuilding should never—and we mean *never*—work out with maximum single-, double-, and triple-rep schemes during the first year of training. There is just too much chance of incurring microscopic tears in the ligaments, muscles, and tendons. The only time you will perform singles, doubles, and triples is during those times when you need to determine what your current one-rep maximum is in a particular lift. This should be done only once every four to six weeks.

Frank Zane, a three-time Mr. Olympia winner, once said, "Your muscles don't have a brain, so they are forced to respond when you jolt or surprise them while training."

With this thought in mind, it is a good idea to mix up your rep pattern every so often in order to develop all of the major components of a muscle cell equally.

Do 8–12 reps (80 percent of max). Then, after a short rest, do 6–8 with 84–88 percent of max and finally 15–25 with 60–78 percent of max. What we are suggesting here is that you do a specific warm-up, then do your low-rep scheme, then finish off with the high-rep scheme last. Why? If you perform your high reps at the beginning of an exercise, there is a marked increase of lactic acid buildup, and as a result you will not receive the maximum force from the myofibrils later on in the low-rep/high-poundage scheme.

When training for strength, you should pause only briefly (one or two seconds) between reps, during which time a small amount of blood is allowed to circulate into the muscles being exercised and thus delay fatigue from lactic acid buildup.

Regarding high-rep training, you could use definite pauses of 5–10 seconds between reps with good results, though at other times you could allow brief pauses of 1–2 seconds between your reps as a means of stressing your muscles differently.

Always use strict form in your repetition movement. Anything less than this will only create a faulty exercise technique.

Former Olympia winner Larry Scott has a rather unique training philosophy when dealing with the subject of reps and sets. To him, "every rep is a set, and every set is a series," which means that each rep is really thought through carefully. The weight that he uses is so close to being the maximum weight that soon each rep is like a set because of the intense concentration that he puts into each particular repetition.

If you can get this concept burned into your mind and train with this type of *mental attitude*, then you are sure to achieve the utmost from your reps and sets.

Remember to perform your reps holistically, in the same workout or in different workouts, to develop all the major components of the muscle cell. Along with this, you must stress the muscle cell with a *variety* of exercises for a particular muscle, working the inner, outer, upper, and lower aspects of it.

Training with as much variety as possible will in many cases alter the shape and appearance of a muscle through the increased development of the various muscle cell components.

A Brief Comment About Reps

It has been stated repeatedly by many authorities in bodybuilding circles that

Juliette Bergman performs incline dumbbell presses for her chest.

the last two reps of a particular set are the most productive for causing an adaptive response in a muscle.

We certainly have no argument with this statement, and here is the reason. Suppose you wanted to do a set of bench presses for 8–12 reps. You would more than likely use a poundage that is near 80 percent of your current 1-rep maximum single attempt.

For all general purposes, let's assume that your max in the bench press is 400 pounds. Eighty percent of 400 pounds is 320 pounds. The very first rep with 320 pounds will be quite easy, because you are capable of exerting 400 pounds of force. On the second rep you may be capable of 392 pounds of force; on the third rep 384 pounds of force. Based on a 1-rep maximum of 400 pounds, your muscles' momentary ability to produce force decreases by 2 percent, or 8 pounds, per each additional rep. By the time you reach the 10th or 11th rep of the set, you have the capability to produce only 328 pounds, or as little as 320 pounds of force, with the final 12th rep being an all-out effort just to complete the lift.

It is these last 2 or 3 reps in which your momentary ability to produce force was near the 100 percent of maximum intensity with the 320 pounds. Now if those last 2 or 3 reps are the reps producing the most adaptive response in the muscles, why not use the 400-pound maximum and perform just 1 rep with it? Then you would be producing maximum force on this 1 rep without having to go through the numerous other reps.

This quandary is not quite that simple to solve, because exercise physiology tests have determined that a muscle should be subject to a contractural force for a minimum of 36 seconds to produce increases in *size* and *strength*.

Therefore, if you are following the generally accepted requirement of moving the weight *up* through the positive or contracted phase of the movement (generally requiring 2 seconds) and then lowering it *down* through the negative phase (taking 4 seconds or more, but not more than 10 seconds), then one all-out maximum effort does not reach the minimum of 36 seconds for increased size and strength.

A single attempt repetition *will not* contribute to an increase in size and strength. It will only reveal to you your current level of strength.

A single attempt should *never* be performed by beginners—only by intermediate and advanced bodybuilders, and then only every four to six weeks at the very most.

For those of you who are interested in the correct way to perform a single on a submaximum level, you must first do a couple of warm-up sets for the particular multijoint exercise you plan on doing. This might very well be the squat, bench press, or deadlift.

After a good warm-up, begin by performing 3–4 sets of 6 reps with 84–88 percent of your current 1-rep maximum. Rest about 3 minutes between each set. After you have finished these sets, perform 1 set of 3 reps with 92 percent of your maximum. Rest as advised previously, and then perform 1 rep with 97 percent of your maximum.

Now decrease the poundage by 3 percent (to 94 percent) and perform another single, then 91 percent, 87 percent, and 84 percent for one single at each of these listed percentages. These single attempts may look easy on paper, especially when you have already done multiple reps with some of these listed percentages. The slight difference here is that instead of resting 3 minutes as between the sets of triples, you will only rest 30 seconds between each single attempt.

A Brief Comment About Sets

Overtraining is caused by doing too many sets and/or exercises per body part. You *can't* overwork on any one set of an exercise, so with this thought in mind, "attack" each set as if it is the only one you are going to be doing for that particular exercise.

The number of sets you perform for an exercise will be determined by your bodybuilding classification, be it beginner, intermediate, or advanced. This important information is explained in Chapter 4, "Structuring a Workout Schedule."

Rest between sets is also an important consideration and should meet the time factors listed in the holistic training guide that follows.

THE HOLISTIC TRAINING GUIDE

REQUIREMENTS	ENDURANCE	STRENGTH/ENDURANCE	SIZE/STRENGTH	POWER
Work Loads	60-78% of 1-rep maximum	80% of 1-rep max	84-88% of 1 rep maximum	88-92% of 1-rep maximum
Repetitions	15-30	8-12	6-8	3-5
Sets	2-6	3-4	3-5	3-4
Speed of each Rep				
I. Positive (Up)	2 or 10 seconds	2 seconds	2 seconds	EXPLOSIVE
II. Negative (Down)	4 seconds	4 seconds	4 seconds	2-4 seconds
Pause Between Reps	5-10 seconds or option: 1-2 seconds	1-2 seconds	1-2 seconds	1-2 seconds
Rest Between Sets				
a. General Exercise	1½-2 minutes	2-3 minutes	3-6 minutes	3-8 minutes
b. Specific Exercise	1-1½ minutes	1-2 minutes		
c. Tendon Exercise			3-8 minutes	3-8 minutes
Rest Between Body Parts in a Workout	Minimal	Minimal	Minimal	Minimal
Rest Days Between Muscle Groups				
1. Thighs		2-3 days	Same	5 days
2. Lower Back		2-3 days	Same	5 days
3. Chest		2-3 days	Same	3-4 days
4. Latissimus		2-3 days	Same	
5. Trapezius		2-3 days	Same	
6. Deltoids		2-3 days	Same	
7. Biceps		2-3 days	Same	
8. Triceps		2-3 days	Same	
9. Forearms		2 days or less	Same	
10. Calves		2 days or less	Same	
11. Abdominals		2 days or less	Same	
12. Neck		2 days or less	Same	
Exercise per Body Part				
a. Beginner	Optional	1 Gen Exercise	Optional	None
b. Intermediate	Optional	1 Specific Exercise	1 General Exercise	Optional
c. Advanced	Optional	2 Specific Exercises	1 General Exercise	Optional

Look at the vascularity of Frank Richards—a result of muscle-overloading.

3
TRAINING MECHANICS— MUSCLE OVERLOADING

You can force your muscles to grow through muscle overloading by applying one or more of the following methods as they apply appropriately to a particular exercise you are performing.

POSITIONING HANDS AND FEET

If you are going to experiment with a narrower or wider hand spacing or foot position than you normally use, you should make only a two-inch adjustment once a week. This is the best way for the muscles to adapt to the new stress and to prevent muscle injury and joint strain.

Hand Spacing

You can use a regular medium (shoulder-width) spacing between the hands on a barbell exercise, or you can go to a narrow (six inches or less) hand spacing or a wide (more than shoulder width and, in some cases, collar to collar on a regular exercise bar) spacing between the hands.

Foot Position

Foot position comes into play in various squatting-type exercises and deadlifting-type movements. A medium (12- to 14-inch) spacing between the feet from heel to heel is optimum for a bodybuilder with large thighs and small hips. A wide (16- to 20-inch) spacing between the heels is good for a bodybuilder who might have larger hips and glutes. A narrow (6-inch or less) spacing throws more stress on the quads and hamstrings.

The wider the stance, the farther outward the toes should be pointed. Point the toes outward at 45 degrees on a 16- to 20-inch stance. This aids the power of the muscles involved and helps you maintain balance.

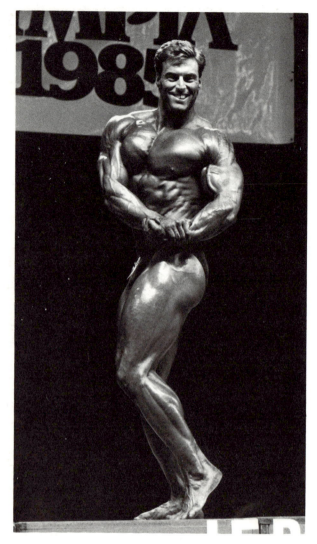

Berry DeMey of Holland.

Gladys Portugues begins a heavy deadlift.

The Grip

The regular method is to place the thumbs around the bar and use the appropriate overhand or underhand grip on the particular exercise you are doing.

If you want to develop a better grip on your deadlifts, you can use an overhand grip (rather than the mixed grip method) and the thumbs around the bar.

Suppose you need an instant answer to your existing grip problems. You can use a hook grip, which uses the thumbs around the bar, but with this variation, tightly wrap the index and middle fingers around the top of the thumbs.

Some bodybuilders find this painful, but the results—sustained gripping strength for exercises like deadlifts, shrugs, and pullups—are worth the little bit of initial suffering.

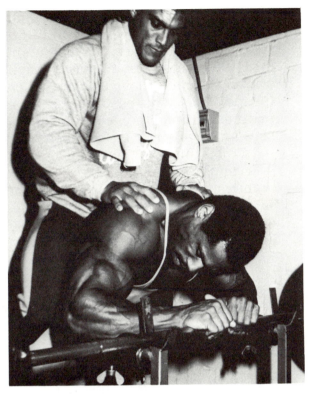

Donkey calf raise—Mike Christian style.

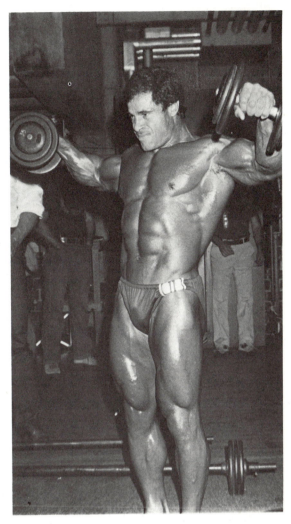

One of Franco Columbu's favorite exercises is the lateral raise.

The thumbless grip (in which the thumbs are on the same side of the bar as the rest of the fingers) is a good way to go with an exercise like palms-up wrist curls. It can be done on triceps pushdown-type exercises and even on the flat or incline barbell bench press. This method relieves pressure and strain on the wrists and forearms and is a good means by which to activate the triceps muscles at the back of the upper arms. It is sometimes known as a "false" grip.

Some strength exponents feel that the triceps account for 75 percent of bench-pressing strength. The problem that arises with the use of the thumbless grip on the bench press is that it is very easy for the barbell to roll out of the hands. Unless you have a capable spotter who might be able to anticipate this situation, it might not be wise to use this particular grip for bench pressing.

DUAL-PURPOSE BENCH TRAINING

For this particular variation in training you will need an exercise bench that doubles as a flat and incline bench. Any exercise that can be performed in a flat or supine position probably can be done in a decline and/or incline position at varying degrees.

You must realize that whenever varying degrees of decline or incline are used the stress or overload on a body part changes somewhat. An illustration of this point is a training secret some champion Olympic lifters used years ago to increase the potential of their standing Olympic overhead press.

They would begin their program by performing flat barbell presses with a weight with which they could do approximately 8–10 reps. This was done for three or four sets. The hand spacing they used throughout the bench press exercise was exactly the same as for the overhead press exercise.

Each week they would increase the incline capacity of the bench by one notch while still attempting to use the same poundage and for the same number of reps and sets as when doing the exercise flat.

After a number of weeks, they were still using the same poundage as when they began the exercise on the flat version, but now they were doing the exercise in a seated upright position. Their overhead press improved dramatically from this training variation.

The stress overloads from this program were as follows. In the initial flat position, the middle pectoralis was the main muscle stressed (though some body-building experts would argue that the bench press is 90 percent front-deltoid stress). As the degree of the incline shifted up to 35–45 degrees, the main emphasis was on the upper clavicular pec. When the incline finally shifted to 90 degrees, the main emphasis changed from the upper pecs to the anterior or front deltoid.

From this example you can get an overview of how stress changes from one segment of a body part to another of the same body part simply by varying the degree of incline or decline the muscle is subjected to.

Imagine how the stress on the biceps changes when dumbbell curls are done in a supine position and then over a period of weeks the movement is changed to a 90-degree incline position, and so on.

EXERCISE STARTING POINTS

If an exercise is being performed in a standing position, can the same exercise be done seated, lying, bent over, or kneeling?

Common sense should help you out on this matter. For example, you can do dumbbell side lateral raises standing, seated, lying prone (face down on a flat exercise bench or even on an incline), bent over (though now you are beginning to stress the rear or posterior delt), and kneeling.

Another idea when using dumbbells is to alternate your exercise movement by doing it first with one arm and then with the other, but at other times doing the movements simultaneously. This process isolates the muscle, going from standing to seated position, because there is less body momentum used in the exercise.

OPTIONAL EXERCISE EQUIPMENT

If an exercise is being performed with a barbell, you can generally replace the barbell with dumbbells. Stimulate your muscles by using a variety of training equipment (if available in a commercial gym, or if you can afford to purchase it for your home gym). Rather than using a straight bar for squatting, switch to a cambered squat bar. For the lats you might use a chinning V bar in the place of a lat pulldown bar or an E-Z curl bar in place of a straight bar for arm work.

Equipment catalogues depict scores of different benches and apparatus to help bodybuilders get the most from their training. One that comes to mind is the Odyssey Rep-Aid bench, which is ideal for the home trainer who wants to get the most out of his bench pressing. Through a clever pulley system, you can *help* your reps along with your feet when you reach a state of failure in the actual pressing of the weight. We feel this is a great advance in home training equipment.

The fabulous Kay Baxter.

QUALITY TRAINING

1. Quality training suggests that, if you are resting for 4 minutes between sets, you should immediately cut the rest periods down to 3½ minutes and then reduce them by a further 30 seconds until you are down to 30 seconds between sets, which overloads the muscle more intensely. Then, each week thereafter, drop 10 seconds from your rest period until you are down to a minimum of 10 seconds of rest.

2. When performing heavy exercises (squats and deadlifts, etc.) in which it is difficult to breathe, take in short, quick gasps of air between the reps to build up a reservoir of oxygen in the blood. Always breathe through the mouth rather than the nose. This will allow more oxygen to reach the lungs.

As you inhale the last breath of air, hold it as you begin the repetition, but begin exhaling two-thirds of the way through the movement to relieve intrathoracic or abdominal pressure. Exhale fully when you reach the lockout or fully contracted position of the rep.

Never hold your breath for prolonged periods because it will cause the blood to back up in the veins. This in turn builds up unnatural pressures within them, which can result in dizziness or blackout from exhaustion and lack of oxygen.

Phil Williams shows remarkable development.

poundages (weights in excess of 84 percent of max).

The way to introduce quality training here is to decrease the number of breaths you are taking from, say, six down to two per rep. If you are already down to two breaths, work to get this down to one breath between repetitions. This will not be as easy as it seems, especially with loads in excess of 84 percent.

PEAK CONTRACTION PAUSES

This method of training intensity calls for you to hold a weight in the fully contracted (concentric) position for several seconds to create as much muscle tension as possible.

Vince Gironda has come up with a slightly different approach to this system, and it involves dumbbell training, where the reps are done in alternate fashion but in a unique way, as follows.

Using the dumbbell overhead press, start with both arms extended and locked out overhead in the fully contracted position. Lower your right arm slowly to your shoulder, then press the dumbbell back to arm's length. Now lower your left arm and press it up in the manner described. This method of dumbbell training can be used on just about any exercise and keeps continuous tension on the muscle.

Then there is a rather limited rep pause technique in which you pause in the bench press (with the weight on the chest) and the squat (parallel position or lower). It is best used with training loads of 80 percent and done on the last set of the exercise (either on the first three or on the final three reps of the set). Example:

On specific exercise movements, breathe rhythmically to the tempo of the exercise. Above we mentioned the value of taking in short, quick gasps of air. In addition to building up a reservoir of oxygen in the blood, this allows you to resummon your mental forces as you psyche up for another rep.

This method will allow you to use slightly more poundage—as well as adding a couple of additional reps—than if you were to take only two or so breaths between reps.

Many bodybuilders will find this a slower and somewhat more pleasant way of getting back into using heavy, heavy

First rep, pause 10 seconds; second rep, pause 5 seconds; third rep, pause 3 seconds.

INCREASE TRAINING POUNDAGES

Sometimes increasing training poundages can turn out to be a monumental task. Even the addition of the smallest conventional barbell plate (1¼ pounds) to each side of a dumbbell or barbell is difficult.

One of the subtler ways some of the bodybuilding champions have described is to add one flat washer (1⅛-inch inside diameter) to each side of the bar at each and every workout. Each washer weighs only ounces, but after you have added a number of these to the bar over a period of a few workouts, you will indeed have worked up to that seemingly impossible 1¼-pound increase on each side of the bar. You can purchase these flat washers at your local hardware store. Be sure to have the salesclerk weigh these for you so you will know how many to buy to make 2½ pounds.

Bob Paris performs the dumbbell press.

Understanding these principles provides a sound base of knowledge that should stay with you throughout your workout schedule and carry you to muscular magnificence.

Matt Mendenhall, Mr. U.S.A.

4
STRUCTURING A WORKOUT SCHEDULE

To begin structuring your own exercise program, you must divide weight training exercises into two classifications:

General

A general weight training exercise is one that works a particular body part from its most favorable or strongest leverage position and receives assistance from other nearby muscle groups. You are able to acquire the most size and strength from general exercises, because it is through these exercises that the greatest poundages or overloads can be utilized with minimal risk of injury.

An example of a general exercise is the bench press. This exercise works the large pectoralis major muscles of the chest. These muscles contribute the largest amount of force (at least 60–70 percent of that muscle's capacity) and movement. The pectoralis major, or any muscle for a particular muscle group that contributes the greatest percentage of force applied, is termed the *prime mover*.

Certain other muscles assist the pectoralis major in applying force in this exercise. In descending order of their assistance, two of them are the anterior deltoid (the muscle segment on the front of the shoulder) and the triceps (the horseshoe-shaped muscle on the back of the upper arm). These two muscles work together (synergistically) with the pecs by helping to apply force in the exercise movement. These helping muscles are called *synergists* or *assistance movers* because they assist only due to their disadvantage in size and strength and do not in most cases contribute to the major force of the movement itself.

Along with the prime movers and the synergists (helping muscles), there are the muscles that hold the body in position, these being many of the other muscles of the body that are not contributing to the force or movement of the exercise.

The ever-popular Tom Platz.

When muscles act in this capacity, they are termed *stabilizers*.

Specific

A specific exercise, sometimes referred to as an *isolation* or *assistance movement*, is one where the function of helping muscles (synergists and stabilizers) is reduced or eliminated.

It is totally impossible to isolate a muscle completely because some other nearby muscles will come into action at some point in the exercise. However, certain machines—Nautilus, Universal, etc.—are able to isolate a muscle or group of muscles more thoroughly than free weights. These machines do reduce the functioning capacities of the synergists and the stabilizer muscles, and this is fine for isolating a muscle, but only if you structure your training so that the majority of your workouts are done with free weights. Free weights coordinate the functions of the synergists and the stabilizers, and this is important to gaining strength.

Many individuals get hung up on using machine weights. For example, there is the bodybuilder who tells you that he can bench press 375 pounds. You inquire as to the method he is using, and he may tell you that he has been using machine weights exclusively for a certain number of months or years. Be assured that if he were to attempt a bench press with free weights he would be fortunate to hit 275 pounds, and if by chance he did you would notice a very uncontrolled movement due to the uncoordinated efforts of the synergists and stabilizers. This happens basically because the machines move the weight through a predetermined path of resistance.

Because the resistance is predetermined in machine weights and certain select specific exercises, the gains in strength are transferable to generalized free weight movements, but only to a slight degree. Why? Because we are dealing with the three dimensions of balance, coordination, and timing. Most specific exercises (except those of the general classification, which are isolated through the process of machine weights) should never be trained at fewer than 8–12 reps per set. The reason is that you are in a restricted leverage position, and the functioning capacity of the synergists and stabilizers has been reduced or greatly eliminated. As a result, the muscles' capacity for really heavy poundages or overloads has been reduced.

For your convenience in selecting exercises for your routine, we are including a detailed exercise selection chart found in Chapter 5, "Body Part Specialization." The exercises listed in Group No. 1 on the chart are the general exercises that will afford you the greatest overall progress in

Deanna Panting of Canada.

this aspect of your training plan.

Regardless of whether you are a beginner, intermediate, or advanced bodybuilder, your bodybuilding exercises will always be structured around the general exercises in Group No. 1.

Unless you are an advanced bodybuilder, avoid getting too involved with many of the specific exercises, except with those for the abdominals. The specific exercises are not absolutely necessary for overall strength development.

Develop the body as a whole unit through general movements. There are three general somato types: *endomorph*, *ectomorph*, and *mesomorph*, and most body structures fall somewhere in between these classifications. But regardless of your body type, the programs we provide will produce muscle-building results for those of you who diligently follow the programs as outlined.

BEGINNER PROGRAMS

These programs are for those who have no weight training experience or have been training for less than one year.

BEGINNER PROGRAMS

	PROGRAM NO. 1	PROGRAM NO. 2
Thighs	Full Squats	Full Squats
Chest	Barbell Bench Press	Barbell Bench Press
Spinae Erector (Lower Back)	Stiff-Legged Deadlifts	
Rhomboids (Middle of Back)	Bent-over Barbell Rows	
Latissimus Dorsi (Outer portion of Upper Back)	Lat Pulldowns	Wide Grip Pullups or Lat Pulldowns
Deltoids	Barbell Overhead Press	Press Behind Neck
Trapezius	Barbell Shrugs	
Biceps	Two-Hand Barbell Curl	Two-Hand Barbell Curl
Triceps	Standing French Press	Standing French Press
Calves	Heel Raises	Standing Heel Raise
Abdominals	Bent Knee Situps	Crunches

Instructions for the 12-Week Program

Perform each weekly program three alternate days, resting Tuesday, Thursday, Saturday, and Sunday. When repetitions are prescribed at 8–12 or 6–8, this is for all the exercises except the abdominals and calves, which can be worked for 15–20 reps per set. Of course, there is an exception made for the squat during weeks 3–7. Use the same poundages for all the sets of a particular exercise unless otherwise advised.

Weeks 1 and 2 Decide which of the above programs you would like to use in your training. Now begin your routine by performing 1 set of each exercise for 8–12 reps. Remember that for best results the exercises should be performed in the exact sequence in which they are listed.

Week 3 Perform 2 sets of 8–12 reps with a fixed poundage (the same weight on all the exercises except the full squat). Example: Bench press: 1 set × 8–12 reps = 100 pounds. Rest, then do 1 set × 8–12 reps = 100 pounds.

On the full squat, do 2 sets of 20 reps, following the instructions given in Chapter 9, "The Champions' Secret—Aerobics."

Weeks 4–7 Continue with your program by performing 3 sets of 8–12 reps of each exercise with a fixed poundage. Do your full squats for 3 sets of 20 reps.

Weeks 8 and 9 Your program remains the same, one exercise per body part for 3 sets of each exercise, but your repetition format changes to:

> Set 1—8–12 reps
> Set 2—6–8 reps
> Set 3—15–20 reps

Because the repetitions scheme is varied on each set, you will not use the same poundage for all three sets. You will increase the poundage for set 2 and decrease the poundage for set 3. During this

Heavy squats performed by superstar Tony Pearson.

two-week training phase, you can change your squats from 3 × 20 to the above repetition pattern.

Weeks 10, 11, and 12 In the 10th, 11th, and 12th weeks comes a minor change in your workout program. You will now perform 3–4 sets of 6–8 reps after your warm-up for each of the exercises except the lat pulldowns or wide-grip pull-ups. These remain at 3 sets of 8–12 reps each. The first 9 weeks have prepared you for the size- and strength-building program you will begin to follow at this time.

To begin this three-week cycle over, add some weight to your exercises, drop back to 4 sets of 6 reps, and follow through as scheduled in weeks 10, 11, and 12.

Muscle Response Many of you may be wondering just exactly how much longer

WEEK 10		
WORKOUT NO. 1	WORKOUT NO. 2	WORKOUT NO. 3
4 set of 6 reps	1 set of 7 reps	1 set of 8 reps
	3 sets of 6 reps	3 sets of 6 reps
WEEK 11		
1 set of 8 reps	2 sets of 8 reps	2 sets of 8 reps
1 set of 7 reps	2 sets of 6 reps	1 set of 7 reps
2 set of 6 reps		1 set of 6 reps
WEEK 12		
3 sets of 8 reps	3 sets of 8 reps	4 sets of 8 reps
1 set of 6 reps	1 set of 7 reps	

Even relaxed, Lee Haney is the personification of mass.

than the above 12-week cycle you must train in order to graduate to an intermediate bodybuilding program. This is determined primarily by your muscle response, which is the amount of time it takes you to see some definite results such as gains in size and strength, body fat losses, etc. For a beginner, this normally will last from three months to one year. At the conclusion of this chapter we have included a strength standard chart so that you may determine to some degree whether you are a beginner, intermediate, or advanced bodybuilder.

INTERMEDIATE PROGRAMS

The intermediate bodybuilder should choose one general exercise, 4 sets of 6–8 reps each, and one specific exercise for each body part, doing these for 3–4 sets of 8–12 reps each. When you choose a specific exercise, be sure that it is for the muscle segment needing the most development. For example, if your quadriceps are well developed and your adductors are in need of some extra size, it wouldn't make sense to choose a specific quad exercise as your second exercise for a body part; rather, you should be looking toward those specific exercises that develop the adductors.

	PROGRAM NO. 1	PROGRAM NO. 2
Thighs	Full Squats Leg Extensions	Full Squats Leg Curls or Squat Lunge
Chest	Supine Bench Press Supine Dumbbell Flyes	Incline Bench Press Incline Dumbbell Flyes
Spinae Erectors	Bent-Knee Deadlifts Good Morning Exercise	Stiff-Leg Deadlifts Prone Hyperextensions
Latissimus Dorsi	Lat Pulldowns Prone Dumbbell Rows on a 20 inch high bench	Lat Pulldowns 45 Degree Lat Pulley Rows
Deltoids	Press Behind Neck (seated) Dumbbell Side Laterals (seated)	Dumbbell Overhead Press Dumbbell Side Laterals
Biceps	Standing Barbell Curl Incline Dumbbell Curls	Dumbbell Curls (seated) Seated Preacher Curls
Triceps	Parallel Bar Dips Long Pulley Tricep Ext.	Standing French Press Tricep Pushdown on Lat Machine
Calves	Standing Calf Raise Donkey Calf Raise Ext.	Standing Calf Raise Seated Calf Raise
Abdominals	Bent-Knee Incline Situps Hanging Leg Raises	Bent-Knee Incline Situps Knee Pullins or Crunches

Instructions

Program No. 1 is a good all-around inter-mediate program for men, and Program No. 2 will meet the needs of female body-builders. The general exercises are done for higher sets and lower reps, 4 sets of 6–8 reps, while the specific exercises are done for lower sets and high reps, 2–3 sets of 10–12 reps, with the exception again being the abs and calves, which use the rep scheme listed in the beginner program.

These programs should be performed two or three times weekly. With this in mind, it would be a good idea to split up your workouts so that you can give each body part a good hard workout. Variations 1, 7, 8, 9, and 10 found at the end of the chapter will most adequately meet these needs.

Wide grip pulldowns performed by Ms. Olympia, Corinna Everson.

Bob Birdsong and Mary Roberts display impressive side-chest poses.

ADVANCED PROGRAMS

	1ST MO. SETS, REPS	2ND MO. SETS, REPS	3RD MO. SETS, REPS
MONDAY - THURSDAY (DELTS AND ARMS)			
Dumbbell Overhead Press	8	10	12
Seated Barbell Front Arm Raise	4 × 10	4 × 12	4 × 15
Expander Cable Chest Pull	14	14	14
Do the above three in triset fashion			
Seated Barbell Curl	8	10	12
Lying Barbell French Press	4 × 8	10	12
Scott Barbell Curl	10	12	15
Tricep Pushdowns	12	15	15
Do the above in four giant set fashion			
Barbell Wrist Curls (palms up)	3 × 12	3 × 13	3 × 14
Squeeze Rubber Ball	3 to failure	3 to failure	3 to failure
TUESDAY - FRIDAY (LEGS AND ABS)			
Olympic-Style Squats	6	8	10
Leg Curls	4 × 10	12	14
Leg Extensions	12	12	15
Do the above three in triset fashion			
One-Leg Heel Raise	5 × 14	17	20
Donkey Calf Raise	14	17	20
Lying Leg Raises	5 × 15	20	25
¼ Twisting Crunch Situps	20	25	30
Superset the two ab exercises			
WEDNESDAY - SATURDAY (BACK AND CHEST)			
Bent-Knee Deadlifts	4 × 10	4 × 8	4 × 6
Barbell Shrugs	10	8	6
Stiff-Arm Pullovers	4 × 12	4 × 15	5 × 20
Lat Machine Pulldowns	10	12	15
OR			
Barbell Bent-over Rowing	8	10	10
Barbell Bench Press to Neck	8	10	12
Flat Bent-Arm Flyes	4 × 15	4 × 15	5 × 15
Gironda "Pec" Dips	4 to failure	4 to failure	5 to failure

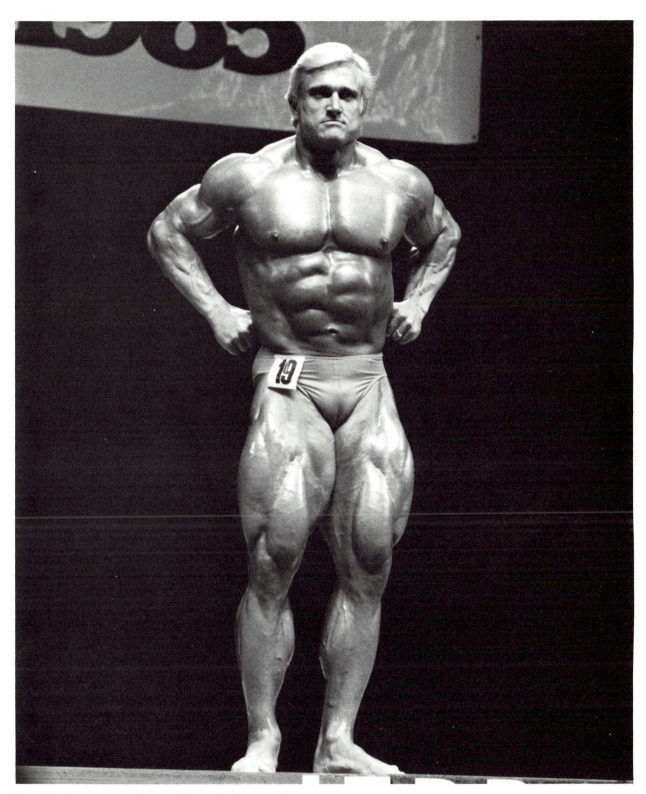

Tom Platz prepares to go into a lat spread.

STRENGTH STANDARDS FOR MEN

BODY WEIGHT	FULL SQUAT	BENCH PRESS	DEADLIFT	STANDING PRESS	BARBELL CURL
105-120	310	260	360	170	70
121-135	340	285	390	190	85
136-155	370	310	420	210	105
156-170	400	335	450	230	120
171-185	430	360	480	250	135
186-205	460	385	510	265	155
206-225	490	410	540	275	175
226-245	520	430	570	285	195
246-Plus	550	440	600	295	205

STRENGTH STANDARDS FOR WOMEN

A Special Note To Women Regarding The Above Chart

Women have 56 percent of the strength of a man in their upper torso. In order for a women to determine whether she has achieved the beginner's GOAL of 60 percent of the standard 1-rep maximum in the bench press, she must take the following steps.

For example, the bench press for a 105-120 person is 260 pounds. A female must first multiply 56 percent times the 260-pound figure. This equals 146 pounds. Now the female lifter can take 60 percent of the 146 pounds to determine whether or not she has reached the beginner's goal. In this case her goal as a beginner is 88 pounds.

Regarding the strength levels of the lower torso, a woman has 72 percent of the strength of a man. The mathematical procedure follows the same steps as cited for the upper torso. Remember that you will use 72 percent and not 56 percent.

ADVANCED PROGRAMS

Advanced training programs allow you a wide range of choices from which to put together a routine. The workout schedule outlined above serves only as a model.

The advanced bodybuilder in many cases will select one general and two specific exercises per body part when setting up a workout program. Also, variations 11–15 of the split system offer the bodybuilder much-needed rest between the various routines.

The usual mode for sets and reps at this stage in the bodybuilder's career allows 4 to 5 sets per exercise and the reps can be varied as suggested in Chapter 2, "The Science of Reps and Sets."

Don't be intimidated by these strength standards. A beginner's goal should be 60 percent of each standard lift for one-rep maximum. For example, a bodybuilder who weighs 156–170 should be able to full squat 240 pounds for one rep.

Do not advance to the intermediate programs until you can perform all of the above lifts at the minimal 60 percent.

An intermediate bodybuilder's goal should be 80–85 percent of each standard lift for a one-rep maximum. Once these intermediate goals have been achieved, it is time to begin an advanced training program.

The advanced bodybuilder's goals are a lifetime summation of training and can equal or exceed the above strength projections.

Understanding the Split Routine System

Some of you may find that due to the length of your workouts (this most generally occurs at the intermediate and advanced levels of bodybuilding) you can no longer train the entire body in one training session and maintain maximum energy and muscle tension levels. An acceptable solution to this problem is to

Jusup Wilcosz demonstrates the machine lateral raise.

VARIATIONS OF THE SPLIT SYSTEM

	MONDAY	TUESDAY	WEDNESDAY	THURSDAY	FRIDAY	SATURDAY	SUNDAY
1	Upper Body	Lower Body	Upper Body	Lower Body	Upper Body	Lower Body	Rest
2	Upper Body	Lower Body	Rest	Upper Body	Lower Body	Rest	Rest
3A	Upper Body	Lower Body	Upper Body	Rest	Lower Body	Upper Body	Rest
3B	Lower Body	Upper Body	Lower Body	Rest	Upper Body	Lower Body	Rest
4	Upper Body	Lower Body	Upper Body	Lower Body	Rest	Rest	Rest
5	Lower Body	Upper Body	Lower Body	Upper Body	Rest	Lower Body	Upper Body
6	Lower Body	Upper Body	Rest	Lower Body	Upper Body	Lower Body	Upper Body
7	Chest, Delts Upper Back, Triceps, Abs, Forearms	Thighs, Calves, Lower Back, Biceps	Same as Mon	Same as Tues	Same as Mon & Wed	Same as Tues & Thur	Rest
8	Chest, Back, Delts, Calves Abs, Forearms	Thighs, Arms, Abs	Same as Mon	Same as Tues	Same as Mon & Wed	Same as Tues & Thur	Rest
9	Thighs, Back, Abs, Forearms, Biceps	Chest, Delts, Triceps, Abs, Calves	Same as Mon	Same as Tues	Same as Mon & Wed	Same as Tues & Thur	Rest
10	Delts, Biceps, Forearm, Calves	Chest, Back, Legs, Abs	Same as Mon	Same as Tues	Same as Mon & Wed	Same as Tues & Thur	Rest
11	Chest, Back, Delts	Biceps, Triceps, Forearms	Thighs, Calves	Same as Mon	Same as Tues	Same as Wed	Rest
12	Chest, Back, Calves, Abs	Delts, Biceps, Triceps, Abs	Thighs, Calves, Forearms	Same as Mon	Same as Tues	Same as Wed	Rest
13A	Chest, Back, Arms	Legs, Waist	Delts	Same as Mon	Same as Tues	Same as Wed	Rest
13B	Delts, Arms	Legs, Waist	Chest, Back	Same as Mon	Same as Tues	Same as Wed	Rest
13C	Chest, Arms	Back, Delts	Legs, Waist,	Same as Mon	Same as Tues	Same as Wed	Rest
14A	Chest, Delts, Triceps, Abs	Rest	Thighs, Calves, Back, Biceps	Rest	Chest, Delts, Triceps, Abs	Rest	Rest
14B	Thighs, Calves, Back, Biceps	Rest	Chest, Delts, Triceps, Abs	Rest	Thighs, Calves, Back, Biceps	Rest	Rest
15A	Chest, Abs, Calves	Delts, Arms	Rest	Thighs, Back, Abs	Chest, Calves, Abs	Rest	Delts, Arms, Abs
15B	Thighs, Back, Abs	Rest	Chest, Calves, Abs	Delts, Arms, Abs	Rest	Thighs, Back, Abs	Chest, Calves, Abs

train certain body parts on one day and then do the remainder on another day. This is commonly known as the *split system* of training.

The split system of training is one of the most successful bodybuilding principles going today, and it is with this in mind that we provide you variations of the system on the following chart.

One of the most popular split-system variations is the *push/pull* system listed as 14A and 14B on the chart. The immediate advantage of this system is that you can work all the pulling muscles (e.g., latissimus, biceps) on one workout day and then do the pushing muscles (e.g., pectoralis, deltoids) on another scheduled day. As it is set up on the chart you will have a 72-hour rest cycle between the pushing or pulling muscles, which may be of particular advantage if you are a low energy type or an ectomorphic-somatotype bodybuilder.

Split-System Options

1. Variations of the split system that list a body part in general terminology,

Samir Bannout and Albert Beckles, two superbly built bodybuilders.

such as *legs* rather than *thighs*, always include exercises for the calf. Likewise, the general term *back*, rather than the specific word *lats*, always includes exercises for the lats, traps, and lower back. The term *arms* rather than *biceps* should always include biceps, triceps, and forearms.

Variations

2. 3A—Works the upper body three days during the week, while the lower body is worked only twice. The following week, 3B, the lower body is worked three times and the upper body twice.

3. 5—Work four days, then rest one day, then work out two successive days in variation 5 and two days in variation 6, then one day of rest.

4. 7, 8, 9, or 10—Can be performed as

Brian Homka and Scott Wilson at Gold's Gym in San Jose, California.

Ali Mala performs lat pulldowns at World's Gym in Venice, California.

scheduled for a three-week duration, then changed over to a twice-per-week body part schedule, using Wednesday, Saturday, and Sunday as your rest days.

5. 2, 7, 8, 9, 10—Could be changed into an A & B workout plan. For example, in variation 7, we will term Monday's workout as A and Tuesday's as workout B. Rest on Wednesday. Continue on Thursday with workout A. Each succeeding week for a month, your workout and rest days will be different. Here is how your schedule for the next four weeks might look.

6. Follow 13A for one week, then 13B the following week, and on the third successive week 13C.

7. This is a push/pull system and is a rotation for recuperation cycle in which you have a 72-hour rest cycle between

	MON	TUES	WED	THUR	FRI	SAT	SUN
Week No. 1	A	B	Rest	A	B	Rest	A
2	B	Rest	A	B	Rest	A	B
3	Rest	A	B	Rest	A	B	Rest
4	A	B	Rest	A	B	Rest	A

CHAMPIONSHIP DOUBLE AND TRIPLE SPLIT ROUTINES

16	A.M. Chest, Back, Calves, Abs P.M. Delts, Biceps, Triceps, Abs	A.M. or P.M. Thighs, Calves, Forearms	Same as Mon	Same as Tues	Same as Mon & Wed	Same as Tues & Thur	Rest
17	A.M. Neck, Forearms	A.M. Calves P.M. Thighs, Chest, Delts, Biceps, Triceps	Same as Mon	A.M. Calves P.M. Legs, Triceps, Delts	Same as Mon & Wed	A.M. Calves P.M. Thighs, Chest, Delts, Biceps, Triceps	Rest
18	A.M. Biceps, Triceps, Forearm P.M. Delts, Neck	A.M. Chest P.M. Lats	A.M. or P.M. Thighs, Calves, Abs	Same as Mon P.M. Same as Mon	A.M. Same as Tues P.M. Same as Tues	A.M. or P.M. Same as Wed	Rest
19	A.M. Arms P.M. Delts, Neck	A.M. Chest P.M. Back	A.M. Legs P.M. Abs	A.M. & P.M. Same as Mon	A.M. & P.M. Same as Tues	A.M. & P.M. Same as Wed	Rest
20	Morn: Chest Noon: Delts Eve: Triceps	Morn: Legs Noon: Back Eve: Biceps	Same as Mon	Same as Tues	Same as Mon & Wed	Same as Tues & Thur	Rest

---

body parts. Perform 14A as outlined, then do 14B the next week, then go back to 14A the following week, etc.

8. For variation 15A and 15B, work out two days in a row, then rest one day.

9. Variations 16, 17, 18, 19, and 20 should be followed only by bodybuilders who have been training on a regular basis for the past five years.

10. Variation 20 is the triple split method that Chuck Sipes (former Mr. Olympia contender) used in preparation for his sensational win at the IFBB Mr. World competition some years ago.

Rich Gaspari uses muscle specialization techniques to develop his massive, ripped back.

5
BODY-PART SPECIALIZATION

Bodybuilding specialization is a method by which you work for advanced development of a certain body part that is lagging in size, strength, or shape or that just needs trimming down.

Theoretically, if you exercise all the body parts equally hard, in time everything will balance out. However, while every major muscle group should develop equally, in proportion to its potential, you will soon discover that some of your body parts are more responsive to training than others.

Generally, rapidity of muscle growth looks like this (most responsive to the least): lats, pecs, biceps, triceps, thighs, obliques/abs, delts, calves, and forearms. When you notice that a particular muscle area is not responding as it should, specialization is the order of the day for bringing that lagging body part up to par.

Before we make any specific recommendations regarding proper specialization techniques, a number of points relat-ing to the aesthetics of bodybuilding should be brought to your attention. There are four qualities you must look for: separation, definition, shape, and symmetry. These are defined briefly as follows.

Separation—This is where one muscle segment disjoins from another and there is a visible display of the musculature, such as the visible division between the lateral deltoid and the posterior deltoid.

Definition—Other terms are synonymous with this, such as *cut* and *ripped*, but all of the terms mean that the skeletal muscles of the body are highly visible through the skin, due in part to the reduction of body fat and water under the skin's surface.

Shape—Simply, each muscle has a point of origin and a point it inserts. You can't change a short muscle into a long one. That is, you cannot completely change the basic contour or shape you were born with, but you *can* alter the

Lat machine pulldowns by Lance Dreher.

cellular component of a particular muscle. This aspect of training is discussed in Chapter 2, "The Science of Reps and Sets."

Symmetry—This is the equal and even development of a muscle on a vertical axis and proportional development on a diagonal axis. The calf and neck, for example, should be balanced proportionately by the upper arm.

All the major individual muscle groups of the body are composed of one or more heads or muscle segments. For ex-

ample, the triceps consist of three heads: the outer head and the inner tricep, which consists of the long head and medial head. While the triceps may seem to be of equal proportional development or balance with other muscles of the body, it may not be so within the tricep itself. Most pressing exercises for the chest and shoulders will tend to activate the long head of the tricep (synergist) to a degree. As a result, the outer and medial head muscles may be disproportionately smaller than the long head. Consequently, the symmetry of the total tricep is thrown off. You must take the necessary steps to correct this by focusing some quality priority training on the outer and medial heads while decreasing the work load on the long head of the tricep.

For reference and a breakdown of the muscle groups and the exercises that work a particular segment of a muscle group, refer to the exercise chart at the end of this chapter. We also suggest that you purchase a copy of *Secrets of Advanced Bodybuilders* from Health for Life, 8083 Sunset Blvd., Suite 483, Los Angeles, CA 90046. We have found this to be one of the best sources, written with the bodybuilder in mind, on the subject of the mechanics of human movement.

ABCS OF SPECIALIZATION

There are a number of ways to incorporate a specialization program into your weekly exercise routine:

1. Put your specialization program at the very beginning of a scheduled daily workout. Generally, your energy level and mental attitude toward training are at their optimum levels at this time, and as a result you will be able to apply maximum training effort to your program of specialization.

2. The next way to structure your specialization is to perform it in the morning and then come back later in the day and complete the remaining workout for the number of other body parts you planned on working that particular day. This incorporates the principle of double-split training.

3. Perform your specialization routine on the days that are not scheduled for a workout. For example, if you train the total body on Monday, Wednesday, and Friday, you can do the specialization program on Tuesday, Thursday, and Saturday.

Guidelines

- Unless otherwise advised, specialization procedures should not be performed more often than every other day in a weekly situation. The exceptions to this are the abdominals and calves,

Double biceps—Mike Christian style.

The world's greatest "most muscular."

training and probably not more than six weeks. This is only a rough average, and there have been cases where bodybuilders have been able to shock a stubborn body part into a new dimension of growth with as little as two weeks of specialization training. A classic example of this is three-time Mr. Olympia Frank Zane, who has been known to bring up a lagging body part in as little as two weeks of concentrated priority training. Arnold Schwarzenegger, on the other hand, would specialize in a body part for as much as nine months at a time.

- Specialization training will normally last six to eight weeks per cycle before mental burnout from the training stress begins to take effect. When you become aware of this condition, you should take a three-week rest from your specialization training before embarking on another priority program for the same body part. This will give you the opportunity to recuperate fully, and your mental attitude toward training will become sharper for the next phase of specialization.

- The remainder of your training program, aside from specialization, should follow this guideline: perform two exercises of four sets on each of your fair body parts and one exercise of four sets on your superior body parts.

- Choose the exercises that will be the most result-producing for the body part needing specialization.

- Maintain a positive mental attitude and the willpower to make the specialization program work.

- It is always best to do a variety of different exercises from *many* different angles to stimulate maximum gains for a lagging body part.

- Specialize in only one body part at a given time.

which can be worked five to six days per week if necessary.

- To begin seeing positive results from a specialization program, you will need a minimum of four weeks of diligent

METHODS OF SPECIALIZATION

One-Day Blitz Method

This is a short-term method that will literally shock your muscles into new growth. You will need to set aside an entire day for this routine, so the best time to do it is on a weekend or any day that is not a scheduled work day at your place of employment.

Set aside 12 hours of this day for your workout; for example, 8:00 A.M. to 8:00 P.M. Using the biceps as an example of a body part in need of specialization, here is how the program might look: Every hour on the hour, perform 3 sets of 6–8 reps of a general exercise, say, the standing two-arm barbell curl. Rest approximately three minutes between sets. On the half-hour,

Ed Kawak: multi Mr. Universe winner.

Juliette Bergman—the belt that fits both the waist and thigh on the same notch.

do 3 sets of 10–12 reps of a specific exercise, such as the one-arm dumbbell concentration curl. Rest 1–1½ minutes between sets.

Due to the time factor involved in this one-day blitz method, it would not be practical (or popular) to do this program in a commercial gym, so here you will find that training in a home gym will be to your advantage.

Be sure to take in approximately 20–30 grams of complete protein every 3–4 hours. You will have very little time to involve yourself with any type of moderate to heavy feeding schedule during the 12-hour blitz method, so keep your protein intake light with such foods as high-protein drinks, yogurt, and cottage cheese. Carbohydrate levels can be assisted by eating fresh fruits.

No doubt, you can come up with some terrific exercise combinations of your own, especially if you review the Exercise Selection Chart at the end of this chapter. And it will be well worth the effort: solid lasting gains of one-half inch or more can

Chicago's favorite cop, Sergio Oliva, works on his chest.

be realized on this program when followed exactly as outlined.

Zane's Method

A method of specialization that three-time Mr. Olympia Frank Zane has found to be useful is as follows.

Using the back, for example, take a heavy workout on Monday, performing 25 sets (5 exercises/5 sets per exercise). On Tuesday, using different exercises, drop from 5 sets to 3 sets per exercise. On Wednesday, do 10–15 overall sets for the back, using the same exercises as for the Tuesday routine. Rest on Thursday. On Friday, hit the back in the same way as for Monday's routine. On Saturday, do a minimal amount of back work, maybe 3–4 sets of some lat stretches. Rest on Sunday.

Training the back in the manner described for two continuous weeks will really bring startling improvement to this area. On a short-term blitz program of this nature, two weeks is about the maximum amount of time for which you can expect to obtain decent results. Since you will be working the back hard five times per week, you may find it to your advantage to do it separately from the rest of your daily exercise routine, perhaps utilizing the daily double-split principle.

BODYBUILDING SPECIALIZATION PROGRAMS

Follow a particular program every other day for four to six weeks, except for the abdominals and calves, which can be trained five to six days per week if necessary.

The incredible legs of Rich Gaspari—a result of muscle specialization.

THIGHS

NO. 1 (OVERALL MUSCLE SIZE)		SETS		REPS
Parallel Squats		2	×	8
		2	×	6
		2	×	4
		2	×	2
Quarter Squats		4	×	10
Nonlock Leg Presses		6	×	6
NO. 2 (QUADRICEPS)				
Barbell Front Squats	Superset	5	×	8-10
Leg Extensions		5	×	12
Nonlock Leg Presses		2	×	8-10
Leg Curls		5	×	10-12
NO. 3 (QUADRICEPS)				
Leg Extensions (strict)		2	×	6
		4	×	4
Leg Extensions (strict)	Superset	2	×	8
Body-weight Jumping Squats		2	×	failure
Rest two minutes between supersets.				
Leg Extensions (semicheat)		3	×	12
Leg Curls		3	×	12
Body-weight Jumping Squats		1	×	failure

CALVES

NO. 1	SETS		REPS
Calf Raise on Calf Machine	5	×	20
One-Leg Calf Raise (hold heavy dumbbell in one hand)	4	×	20

After you have performed the above two exercises for the required sets and reps, lean against a wall and rise up on your toes (with just your own body weight) while flexing the calves very hard in the top contracted position for a 10- to 20- second count. Do this four times, pausing to rest slightly between sets.

After each set of 10 full reps, finish off with 20 burns in the high or top contracted position of the movement.

NO. 2	SETS		REPS
Calf Raise on Calf Machine	4	×	25
One-Leg Calf Raise (body-weight only)	4	×	60

On the first 30 reps, concentrate on the downward stretch. Do the final 30 reps in a bouncy fashion, concentrating on the high flex position.

Sit on a high bench so that the legs are free to hang. Now work the feet back and forth. Add poundage to the exercise when the reps become easy, but don't sacrifice form just for the sake of adding poundage.

Sergio Olivia and Bob Paris.

No. 3

The following calf program will incorporate the staggered set principle in that you will select two calf exercises and perform one set of a calf exercise between sets of another body part exercise until you have completed 10 sets of each calf exercise. For example, if you are scheduled to perform the bench press for 5 sets, you will perform one set of a selected calf exercise between the sets of bench presses. Then the next exercise may be roman chair squats for 5 sets, and here you would alternate a set of roman chair squats with a set of calf raises. At the conclusion of 5 sets of roman chair squats you will have completed 10 sets of your first calf exercise. Simply follow the above instructions for your second calf exercise by inserting sets of the calf exercise between other sets

Sensational Corinna Everson works her quads.

of other body part exercises until you have completed 10 sets.

Go heavy on your sets by beginning with 20 reps per set and progressively add poundage to each remaining set until you can perform only 3 reps on the 10th and final set of a particular calf exercise.

The next day you will follow this prin-ciple in like manner, only here you will add reps and not poundage. Start with 20 reps and work to the highest reps possible by the 10th and final set of each selected calf exercise.

This is a six-day program. Three days will be heavy, and three alternate days will be termed light–high rep days. If for some reason your staggered set program falls on a scheduled rest day, perform the 10 sets of each in a multipoundage fash-ion for a heavy day and in cumulative rep fashion on the light days. Staggered sets can be applied to any body part you might choose.

No. 4

This calf program is a crash program that can be used for short, intense periods as a shock treatment for the calf muscle. The program is intended to blitz the calves into new growth and utilizes just one calf exercise for the entire program.

The following calf program is to be performed for 15 days in a row and in the manner described.

On day 1 you will perform 5 sets of the selected calf exercise. Then each day, for the next 15 days, you will add 2 additional sets to your program. The set and rep pattern for this program goes something like this: the first 25 percent of the sets will be warm-ups. During the warm-up sets, work very carefully and obtain a maximum stretch in the calf muscle.

The rep pattern for the warm-ups be-gins with a count of 35 for the first set. On each additional warm-up set that you in-

15 DAY CALF BLITZ PROGRAM															
Day	1	2	3	4	5	6	7	8	9	10	11	12	13	14	15
Warm-up Set	1	2	2	3	3	4	4	5	5	6	6	7	7	8	8
Hard-Work Sets	3	3	5	5	7	7	9	9	11	11	13	13	15	15	17
Pump Sets	1	2	2	3	3	4	4	5	5	6	6	7	7	8	8

clude for a particular day, decrease the reps by 5 but only to a minimum count of 15 reps.

After you have completed the warm-up sets, the next 50% of your daily program will constitute the hard-work sets. The reps for this portion of the program are fixed at 10. Use as much poundage as possible and really bear down because these hard-work sets are the key to the success of this program.

The final 25 percent of your program is dedicated to obtaining a maximum pump in the calf region. The rep pattern here is just the opposite of that of the warm-ups in that you will begin with a count of 15 and on each additional pump set you perform increase the rep count by 5, to a maximum of 35.

For the sake of clarity, this program is outlined below for the 15-day duration.

No. 5

This specialization program is almost the opposite of program 4 in that you will be performing just a few sets of a calf exercise, but the secret to this program is the utilization of certain training principles

Tony Pearson does thigh extensions.

such as rest pause, burns, and supersets. When these three training principles are combined in the unique manner about to be described, you can literally shock your calves into a greater dimension of size and shape.

The exercise is the calf on the standing calf machine. Begin with a poundage that will allow you to perform 15 superstrict reps in this exercise. At the completion of the final rep, shake each leg twice alternately (this procedure shouldn't take longer than eight seconds). Immediately perform 8 strict reps and the leg shake procedure. Then do another 8 reps and the leg shake. Now do another 8 reps in the standard calf raise, but this time do not shake the legs; rather, begin to do some burns in the top contracted position. Do these until you find the pain almost unbearable. Now go up into the high contracted position again, then

The mighty Tom Platz squeezes out one more rep.

slowly come down on one foot (this is a one-leg calf raise done as negative rep), then up on two feet and down on the opposite foot. Continue this for 10–20 reps for each leg.

This completes one set. Rest for five minutes (during this time, massage the calves to get the blood moving) and repeat the entire procedure as described for a second set.

This program is to be followed every other day for a period of two weeks. After the initial two-week break-in on this program, extend your sets in the following manner.

After finishing the two-up-and-one-down portion of the set, immediately perform another set of burns and then finish off your set once again with the two-up-and-one-down format.

This program not only works quite well using the standing calf machine but can in fact be utilized on a seated calf machine, if it is your desire to work the soleus muscle in the calf. It might be a good idea to develop this muscle to its maximum as it adds a dimension to the width of the calf, and this in turn adds to the symmetry of the whole leg, especially when viewed from the front.

The incomparable Arnold Schwarzenegger.

LATS

Wide-Grip Pullups to the Chest	5	×	6-8
Heavy Barbell Bent-over Rowing	4	×	6-8
Horizontal Floor Pulley Rows	4	×	8-10
One-Arm Dumbbell Rowing	4	×	8-10

NO. 2

Wide-Grip Pullups to the Chest

Lat Pulldown to the Chest

Long Floor Pulley Lat Rowing

Do these three exercises in triset fashion for 8 reps and 5 burns on each set. Don't rest at all between sets and take only minimal rest between each triset series. Do 4-6 trisets.

One of the most muscular physiques in bodybuilding history belongs to Lou Ferrigno.

John Hynatyschak of the U.S.

CHEST

Bench Press	2	×	6
	2	×	4
	2	×	2
	2	×	1

Superset

Incline Dumbbell Flyes	4	×	12
Incline Barbell Press	4	×	8
Straight-Arm Pullovers	2	×	20

NO.2

Incline Barbell Bench Press	4	×	6
Decline Dumbbell Flyes	4	×	10-12
Incline Dumbbell Press	4	×	6-8
Wide-Grip Gironda Pec Dips	3	×	8-10

NOTES   On the regular bench press in no. 1, use the heavy-light system. Add weight and decrease the reps. The incline barbell press can be performed with a wide grip and held high on the chest (to work the shoulder girdle pec region). Breathe deeply twice between reps. The straight-arm pullover should be performed with light resistance; work for a deep, deep stretch. Stay away from excessive decline movements that work the lower pecs. Muscle tissue buildup in the lower pec region may look good now, but later on in years you may acquire a sagging lower pec line.

TRAPS

NO. 1

Wide-Grip Upright Rowing	4	×	12
Barbell Hang Cleans	4	×	12
High Pulls	4	×	6
Barbell Shoulder Shrugs	4	×	8

NOTES   On the upright rows and the barbell hang cleans, breathe twice between reps. The traps are one of the least likely areas of the body to need specialization.

DELTOIDS

NO. 1

Barbell Seated Front Press	4	×	8
Front Barbell Lateral Raise	2	×	12
Barbell Press Behind Neck (seated)	4	×	8
Side Dumbbell Lateral Raises (standing)	2	×	12
Bent-over Dumbbell Rear Lateral Raise	2	×	10

Mike Christian squeezes into a most muscular.

Al Beckles of England.

NO. 2

Barbell Press Behind Neck	6	×	6
Seated Dumbbell Press on 80-degree Incline Superset	5	×	6-8
Side 1 Dumbbell Lateral Raise on 80-degree Incline Superset	5	×	10
Bent-over Dumbbell Rear Lateral Raise	3	×	10-12

NO.3

Down-the-Rack Dumbbell Presses	Warm up first, then start heavy and work light in 5- to 10-pound jumps. No rest between sets. Do 8 set of 6 reps.
Side Dumbbell Lateral Raises (Standing)	Down-the-rack fashion for 6 sets of 10 reps. No rest between sets.
Bent-over Dumbbell Rear Lateral Raise	Down-the-rack fashion for 6-8 sets of 8-10 reps. No rest between sets.

NOTES   Use a shoulder-width grip on the seated front press and a fairly wide grip on the press behind neck in routine no. 1. On the seated dumbbell press listed in routines 2 and 3, your repetitions should be performed very slowly and with a lot of concentration. On the side standing dumbbell lateral raise in no. 1 and no. 3, be sure to tilt the front end of the bells down as you raise the bells out to the side. Use a slight elbow bend on the lateral movements.

BICEPS

Heavy Barbell Curls	2	×	12
	2	×	6
	2	×	4
	2	×	2
Seated Dumbbell Concentration Curls (one-arm)	2	×	12
Scott (Preacher) Barbell Curls	2	×	12

NO. 2

Scott (Preacher) Barbell Curls Superset	4	×	6
Incline Dumbbell Curls	4	×	6-8
Scott (Preacher) Dumbbell Curls Superset	4	×	6
One-Arm Dumbbell Concentration Curls	4	×	12

NO. 3

Dumbbell Curls on the Preacher Bench	Use maximum weight for 6 reps. Then do 4 burns at the top contracted position of the movement.
Barbell Curls on the Preacher Bench	Use a wide grip for a 6-rep count. Then do 4 burns at the contracted position.
Reverse Curl on the Preacher Bench with an EZ curl bar	Do 6 reps and 4 burns at the top of each rep.

Perform one exercise after the other with absolutely no rest between sets. This is one series. Do 4-6 series.

NO 4.

21 Barbell Curl	5 Sets		
Barbell Cheat Curls	15	×	4

Alternate one set of the 21 curls to each three sets of the barbell cheat curl.

NOTES   On the heavy barbell curls in no. 1, use the heavy-light system. Add weight and decrease the reps. The various scott curls or preacher bench curls in the various programs should be performed slowly.

TRICEPS

NO. 1

Lying French Press	2	×	12
	2	×	8
	2	×	6
	2	×	4
Triceps Pushdown on Lat Machine Superset	2	×	10
One-Arm Dumbbell Tricep Extensions Superset	2	×	10

NO. 2

Lying Tricep Pullover and Press (EZ Curl Bar) Superset	6	×	6
Seated French Press on 80-degree Incline Bench Superset	5	×	8-10
Kneeling (chest on bench) Long Pull Tricep Extensions	5	×	10-12
Triceps Pushdown on Lat Machine	3	×	6

NO. 3

The following tricep routine is a favorite of two-time Mr. Olympia Larry Scott. The routine is *very* hard, but it blows up the triceps incredibly.

Supine Tricep Press Using EZ Curl Bar	8 reps and 4 burns at the top
Long Pull Tricep Extensions	8 reps and 5 burns at the top

Superset these two exercises for 5 sets of 8 reps each (don't forget the burns—they're important). After you have completed this phase of the program, move again to the long pull tricep extension. Do about 8-10 sets, decreasing poundage every 2-3 sets. Try to get your rest periods between sets down to where you are taking only 10 deep breaths between sets.

NO. 4

21 Barbell French Press	5 sets		
Barbell Cheat French Press	15	×	4

Alternate one set of the 21 french press to each three sets of the barbell cheat french press.

On the french press and supine tricep press movements listed in the four routines, keep the elbows pointed up toward the ceiling, making the triceps do the work. The tricep pushdown exercise listed in routine no. 2 is performed as follows: Begin each set with a poundage that will allow you to complete 6 reps. Then drop some poundage (20 percent) and do as many reps as possible and finally another 20 percent decrease and pump to a point of momentary failure. This constitutes one set.

Standing dumbbell presses demonstrated by Erika Mes.

BICEPS-TRICEPS-COMBINATION

NO. 1

Cheat Barbell Curls	4	×	4
Dumbbell Concentration Curl	4	×	8-10
Barbell Scott Curls	3	×	10
Lying French Press	4	×	6
Tricep Pushdowns	3	×	20
Parallel Bar Dips	4	×	8

NO. 2

Cheat Barbell Curls	Superset	4	×	6
Barbell Scott Curls	Superset	4	×	15
Barbell French Press		4	×	12
Parallel Bar Dips		3	×	10

Mohamed Makkawy, Bertil Fox, and Frank Zane.

Norway's Gunnar Rosbo does donkey raises.

BICEPS-TRICEPS-FOREARM COMBINATION

Barbell Scott Curls	2	×	12
Standing Barbell Curls	2	×	12
(light to heavy on these)	2	×	6
	2	×	4
	2	×	2
Alternate Seated Dumbbell Curls	4	×	8
Lying Barbell French Press	Same set and rep scheme as for Standing Barbell Curls		
Rear Bench Dips	4	×	8
One-Arm Dumbbell Tricep Extensions (lying supine on bench)	2	×	12
Standing Barbell Reverse Curls	4	×	10-12
Barbell Wrist Curls (palms up)	2	×	15

FOREARMS

NO.1

Scott Reverse Curls (with EZ curl bar)	4	×	8

Dumbbell Wrist Curl (palms up) with upper arm parallel to the floor	4	×	15
Rubber Expander Cable Curls	4	×	12
Squeeze Rubber Ball	4	×	40

NO.2

Barbell Wrist Curls (palms up)	Superset	6	×	15
Standing Reverse Barbell Curls	Superset	6	×	8
Forearm Gripper Machine		3	×	failure
Wrist Roller		3	×	failure

NOTE   Forearm size and gripping power are very much a matter of intense mental concentration. The dumbbell wrist curl in no. 1 is described in Chapter 8. The wrist roller is primarily for adding size and will do very little for gripping power.

ABDOMINALS

NO. 1

Front Bends (with a broomstick behind the neck)	2	×	100
Side Bends (broomstick behind the neck)	2	×	100
45-degree Incline Situps (bent knee and weight behind head)	2	×	20
Hanging Leg Raises	4	×	15
Seated Body Twists (broomstick behind neck)	2	×	200
Jog ½ mile			

NO. 2

Hanging Leg Raises	4	×	15
Gironda ¼ Crunch Situps	4	×	10
Lying Leg Raise off Bench	4	×	25
Seated Twists with Bar on Shoulder	4	×	100

NOTE   There are a couple of options with these two abdominal programs. You can use program no. 1 or 2 every other day or for a more intense ab workout alternate 1 and 2 every other day six days per week. The front bends listed in no. 1 are performed in the style of a good morning exercise but with the emphasis on tensing the abs constantly.

On the hanging leg raises in no. 1, try taking only six deep breaths between sets. Routine no. 2 is to be performed in giant set fashion.

BODY PROGRAMMING

We realize that many of you might not wish to follow the specific specialization programs outlined in this chapter. For those of you who would prefer to specialize in more or less an instinctive fashion, we include the following guidelines so that you may compute your own specialization program for maximum achievement.

To begin with, it is important that you

follow the "ABCs of Specialization" when planning out your program. The first thing you must do is to appraise the muscle in question. Does it need more size? strength? better shape? a combination of these? Once you have answered these questions, it is time to begin planning your specialization routine, but only if you have made a truthful critique of your physique.

The Exercise Selection Chart in this chapter will be very helpful to you in choosing the proper exercises for specialization.

For overall development (size, strength, and shape), pick two exercises from Group No. 1, two exercises from Group No. 2 (it is important that you realize not only that exercises chosen from this group serve in an isolating and shaping capacity but that many of these exercises are quite functional for assistance work in building that little extra raw strength in a generalized movement), and finally, as an option, one exercise from Group No. 3.

At this point you will have a nice overall balance of two size and power movements, two isolating or shaping exercises, and one optional tendon-building exercise.

Developing maximum strength requires you to put a great deal of training effort into generalized exercises, with the isolating exercises being of a secondary consideration. To meet this requirement you might select two or three general exercises (size and power), one specific exercise (isolating and shaping), and, as an additional option, one exercise from Group No. 3.

For maximum isolation and shaping of a muscle exclusively, you might want to choose one exercise from Group No. 1 and three exercises from Group No. 2.

Another alternative is to select all four

Marjo Selin, Ms. Olympia challenger.

exercises from Group No. 2. This is an effective exercise ratio especially for the female bodybuilder who might decide to go all out on working abductors, adductors, hamstrings, and gluteus.

To determine the number of reps and sets you should use when structuring your own specialization program, refer to the Holistic Training Guide in Chapter 2, "The Science of Reps and Sets."

Body programming is more aptly directed at the advanced bodybuilders who will generally require 18–24 overall sets for a lagging body part and utilize four or five exercises for obtaining maximum size and strength.

Intermediate bodybuilders also may wish to implement a specialization training program, and this is acceptable as long as they follow these guidelines:

1. Use no more than three to four exercises for a total of 12–15 sets on the body part needing the specialization.
2. Perform two exercises of two sets on each of your fair body parts.
3. Perform one exercise of two sets on your superior body parts.

EXERCISE SELECTION CHART

This exercise chart will be helpful in determining exactly which muscle(s) you are working in a particular exercise. Use the chart to help you focus on your lagging body parts.

	GROUP NO. 1 GENERAL SIZE AND POWER	GROUP NO. 2 SPECIFIC ISOLATING AND SHAPING	GROUP NO. 3 TENDON STRENGTH
THIGHS Function: Straightens knee, assists hip joint action	High Bar Olympic Squats Leg Press ½ Squats (Box-Style) Regular Power Squats	One-Leg Squat Roman Chair Squats Sissy Squats	¼ Squats Negatives Power Rack Work Squat Supports
a. QUADRICEPS		Front Squats (works high quad) Hack Squat (works low quad) Jumping Squats Leg Extensions Single-Leg Extension for peak Nonlock Burning Squats	
b. THIGH BICEPS		Leg Curls on machine Standing Single-Leg Curl for peak Stiff-Legged Deadlifts work this muscle segment	
c. ADDUCTORS (Inner Thighs)		Side Squats Wide-Stance Ballet or Frog Squats Supine Leg Splits (iron shoes) Isometric Squeeze with a basketball between upper thighs	

d. ABDUCTORS (Outer Thighs)		Nautilus Inner & Outer Thigh Machine Standing Leg Raise to Side (iron shoes or floor pulley attachment)	
e. SARTORIUS	Various squat movements work it hard and make it thick		
f. GLUTEUS (Reduce)		Squat Lunges One-Leg Swing or Kickback with iron shoes	Power Rack Work

BACK

Function: Draws arms down and back	Bent-over Rowing (Barbell or Dumbbells) Heavy Bent-Knee Deadlifts Power Cleans (Barbell or Dumbbell combination)	Heavy Bent-arm Pullovers Lat Stretches	
a. TRAPS Function: Raise and lower shoulder girdle; moves shoulder blades	Dead Hang Cleans or Snatches High Pulls with barbell Wide-Grip Upright Rowing	Shrugs with barbell or dumbbells	¼ Shrugs (works Rhomboids)
b. UPPER LATS		45-degree Lat Machine Pulldowns Wide-Grip Lat Pulldowns (works long strand of lat) Wide-Grip Pullups (front or back and palms forward) Long T-Bar Leverage Rowing Reeves Alternate Dumbbell Rowing One-Arm Dumbbell Rows	
c. MIDDLE LAT		Horizontal Floor Pulley Rows 7-feet-high Pulley—Sit 10 feet away at 30 degrees) Prone Dumbbell Rows on a 20-inch-high bench Racing Dive Lat Pulls	
d. LOWER LAT	Close-Grip Pullups to Chest Close-Grip Bent-over Rows (palms up and palms down)	Lat Pulldown with a parallel grip— use a Pro-Style Lat Bar or a Nautilus DORSI-BAR for this	
e. SPINAE ERECTORS	Stiff-Legged Deadlifts	Prone Hyperextensions (30-inch-high bench) Good Morning Exercise	

CHEST

Function: Draws arms in, down, and forward across chest

Flat Bench Press with Barbell or Dumbbells	Krusher of Powertwister Dumbbell Around the Worlds Pec Deck Exercises Expander chest pulls	¼ Benches Bench Supports Negatives Expander "chest pulls"

a. UPPER PECS

40-degree Incline Barbell Press to the Neck Incline Press with Barbell or Dumbbells	Incline Flyes with Dumbbells Supine Dumbbell Fly Crossovers High-Cable Crossovers

b. MIDDLE PECS

20-degree Barbell Press to the Neck Barbell or Dumbbell Press (palms facing each other)	Flat Dumbbell Bench Flyes

c. LOWER PECS

Decline Press with Barbell or Dumbbells Decline Barbell Press to Neck	Decline Dumbbell Flyes Gironda Pec Dips Low-Cable Crossovers

d. RIB CAGE

	Straight-Arm Pullovers (light poundages) Barbell or Dumbbells Dislocates with Dumbbells Decline Pullovers with Barbell or single Dumbbell

f. SERRATUS
Function: Rotates shoulder blades down

Overhead Presses and the various Pullovers work this muscle segment	Serratus Pulls on Lat Machine (twisting variety as option)

DELTOIDS

Fumction: Raises arm to horizontal from side, front and a partial assist to the rear

Overhead Press with Barbell or Dumbbells — Standing or Seated Press Behind the Neck (standing or seated) Fore & Aft Press (use a barbell, standing or seated)		Power Rack Work

a. ANTERIOR (Front)

Influenced greatly by the above exercises and all pressing movements for the chest	Standing Front Raise with Barbell or Dumbbells — Alt one Dumbbell at a time Supine Flat-Bench Front Raise with Barbell or Dumbbells

b. LATERAL
(Medial or Side)

Dumbbell Side Laterals
(standing or seated) Cable
Floor Pulley Laterals
(Standing or kneeling) one
or two-Arm
Style
Expander Upright Rowing
(shoulder-width grip). Keep
barbell 12 inches in front of
body.
Cable Floor Pulley Lateral
Raise (standing) one-or
two-Arm Style

c. POSTERIOR
(Rear)

Bent-over Dumbbell Lateral
Raise (90-degree) (Side or
Rear) or with rubber
expanders
Cable Floor Pull Lateral
Raise
(Bent-over 90-degree
position)
Lying Side Lateral Raise with
Dumbbells on 45-degree
Incline Bench
Prone Bench Dumbbell
Raise to Rear

BICEPS

Function: Bends elbow joint and assists in forearm suplination — Heavy Barbell or Dumbbell Curls, Regular-Grip Chins — Expander Cable Curls — Cheat Barbell or Dumbbell Curls

a. HIGH BICEP — Chin ups, close grip (4 inch) palms facing — Barbell or Dumbbell Spider Curls on a vertical 90-degree side of a preacher bench
Seated Close-Grip (4-inch) Bent-over barbell curl
Concentration Dumbbell Curl

b. MIDDLE BICEP — Kneeling Bench Curls
Seated Barbell Curls
Gironda Body Drag Curls — Alternate Supine Dumbbell Bench Curls
45-degree Incline Dumbbell Curls (alt)
Seated Dumbbell Curls

c. LOWER BICEPS — Scott Curls with Barbell or Dumbbells
Hammer Curls (thumbs up) with Dumbbells

The "road map" back of Rich Gaspari.

Berry DeMey shows some impressive abs.

TRICEPS
Function: Extends elbows

a. OUTER TRICEPS (Lateral) — French Press (standing, lying, or seated)
Narrow-Grip (12-inch) Press to Neck

b. INNER TRICEPS
　1. Long Head — Parallel Bar Dips (upright posture)
Seated-Position Dips

　2. Medial Head (near elbow) — Long Pulley Tricep Extension

Expander Cable archer movement

One- Arm Dumbbell Tricep Extension (standing, lying, or seated) one- or two-Arm Dumbbell Kickbacks

Tricep Pushdowns

ABDOMINALS

a. UPPER ABS

Bent-Knee Sit-ups

Stomach Suctions
45-degree Incline Situp with weight behind head
½ Situps
Alternate ½ Situps

b. MIDDLE ABS

¼ Crunches
Twisting ¼ Crunches
Roman Chair Situps (to parallel only)
45-degree Knee Pullins

c. LOWER ABS

Leg Raises (hanging or lying)
Gironda Abdo Hip Roll

d. OBLIQUES
Function: Bends spine forward, sideways

Various Twisting (Standing, Seated, or Bent over) with a broomstick or exercise bar
Side Bends (dumbbell in one hand only)

FOREARMS
Function: Bends, straightens fingers, thumbs and wrist

One-Hand Deadlifts
Zottman Dumbbell Curls
Pinch Gripping
Saxon Grip Exercise

Wrist Roller Movement
Squeeze Rubber Ball
Forearm Gripper Machine
Hand Grippers

a. FLEXORS

Barbell or Dumbbell Wrist Curls with palms up

Decline Barbell Wrist Curl with palms up

b. EXTENSORS

Barbell Reverse Curls

Barbell Wrist Curls with palms down
Decline Barbell Wrist Curl with palms down

Expander Cable Reverse Curls
Preacher Barbell Reverse Curls
Weaver Leverage Bar

CALF
Function: Extends ankle and assists knee flexion

Standing Calf Machine Heel Raise
Leg Press Heel Raise

York Calf Flex Apparatus
One-Leg Calf Raise

a. UPPER CALF

Donkey Calf Raise
Hack Machine Calf Raise

b. FRONT CALF

Tibileous Contractions

c. LOWER CALF

Seated Calf Raise (works the soleus)

Calf Stretching (Boyer Coe style)

NECK
Function: Bends and rotates head, neck; draws head forward

Various Neck Bridges with just your body weight to begin with and advance to using progressive resistance with the NECK STRAP

The true meaning of *Mass*—Barbarian David Paul.

6
OPTIMUM MUSCLE-BLASTING TECHNIQUES

To increase your muscular size and strength, you must methodically impose new demands on your muscles by exceeding previous levels of physical development. There are certain unique and highly stimulating methods of overloading a muscle that will allow you to accomplish this. Here is an explanantion of some of these methods and how to use them effectively for optimum muscle blasting, including a new ultra-effective method rarely written about in bodybuilding publications known as the Jettison Technique.

BURNS

This is a type of partial cramping movement that can be used during and at the end of a set of repetitions for an exercise. In the barbell curl, for example, lower the barbell back about three inches from this top position and immediately curl the barbell back to full tension at the neck. Hold this tension about one-quarter of a second, then lower the barbell back as described and contract to full tension. Each proceeding burn should accumulate more tension than the previous burn.

One way to work burns into your exercise is to perform two complete full-range reps of an exercise, then two burns, and so on, until you have completed your predetermined number of reps for a set. The other way to introduce burns into your rep pattern is to do 6–10 of these in a row at the end of a set, when you can't do any more full-range reps.

CUMULATIVE REPETITIONS

This is an optimum muscle-blasting technique at its best. This technique can be utilized in body-weight-only exercises (incline situps, parallel bar dips, pullups, pushups, seated-position dips, sissy squats, one-leg squats, squat jumps, etc.) and in free-weight exercises.

To illustrate body-weight-only exercises, let's examine the parallel bar dip. This is performed with just your body weight, but in a unique manner. Do 1 rep, rest 2 seconds, do 2 reps, rest 2 seconds, do 3 reps, rest 2 seconds, and continue in this manner until you simply cannot exceed your previous repetition count. For instance, if you get up to 10 reps and find that after a 2-second rest you can't do 11 reps in this exercise, this is where you consider the exercise complete for this particular workout.

The objective here is to accustom the muscles to accommodating more and more reps each workout until you can finish off with 25 reps. When you reach this number, you will have completed 325 cumulative reps overall.

We realize that a majority of the success in completing a body-weight-only exercise is related directly to your weight. If you weigh 175 pounds, you will in most cases have a much better chance of com-

Corinna Everson, Mary Roberts, and Clare Furr flex during the posedown at the 1985 Ms. Olympia.

Incline curls as performed by Tony Pearson.

pleting those 25 repetitions than you would if you weighed 200-plus pounds. If your weight proves prohibitive, there *is* a substitute cumulative repetition technique: follow the program exactly as it is described above but work up to only 10 repetitions and then back down to one.

The instruction for free-weight exercises is somewhat different from that given for a body-weight-only exercise. The exciting part about training with cumulative repetitions as it applies to free weights is the progressive levels you can place on your muscles. This is accom-plished by the repetition scheme you select. Let's assume that you decide to use the high-bar Olympic-style squat for your exercise. The repetition selection you have chosen from the Holistic Training Guide in Chapter 2, "The Science of Reps and Sets," is 3–5 reps for power. Use a poundage that will allow you to blast out these 3–5 reps in proper form. You are now ready to begin. Perform 1 rep of the high-bar Olympic-style squat; then put the barbell back into the squat rack and rest while counting off 10 seconds. Perform 2 reps, then take a 10-second rest; do 3 reps

Ali Mala performs bent-over rows.

and take a 10-second rest, etc., until you can't exceed your prior repetition count.

To clarify this, let's say that you have just worked up to 4 reps and find that after the 10-second rest you can't do 5 reps in the particular exercise. At this point you will terminate the high-bar Olympic style squat for this workout session. Continue from workout to workout using the same poundage until you are able to complete 8 reps successfully. After you have reached this goal, a poundage increase is in order. Add only enough poundage to drop your repetition scheme back down to a base of 3–5 reps and begin this cycle over again. The beauty of this progression scheme is that you are using a repetition count at the beginning (3–5 reps) that maximizes your power, but when you have achieved your goal of 8 reps you are accomplishing strength and size gains with a poundage that is approximately 4 percent greater than you would normally be able to handle.

As you might remember from reading Chapter 4 on structuring a workout schedule, this base repetition (3–5) can be used only with general exercises and in some cases tendon-strengthening movements but never with specific (isolating or shaping) exercises because they will make you so susceptible to injury from maximum low-rep overloads.

The best way to apply the cumulative repetition plan to a specific exercise is to begin with a repetition base of 10 counts and gradually work up to a goal of 15 repetitions. The base strength/endurance-building reps of 10, when taken to a count of 15, will take you into a dimension of endurance training but with a poundage previously used for building strength.

FORCED REPS

A forced rep is an extension of a particular set of repetitions in which your strength level at the beginning of the set has been reduced to a point of positive failure (where you can no longer move the weight under your own power).

To clarify this, let's assume that you have chosen to perform a set of flat barbell bench presses for 8–12 reps. Your best maximum single attempt at the present time might be 300 pounds. A quick look at the Holistic Training Guide indicates that you should use 80 percent of 300 pounds in order to accomplish an 8- to 12-rep scheme.

You begin to bang out the reps with the 240 pounds. Taking into account the high and low reps (8 to as many as 12 reps with 80 percent of a 1-rep max), you might hit the point of positive failure on the 11th rep. You are simply not strong enough to accomplish reps 11 and 12 because your strength has been reduced to under 240 pounds. A training partner immediately helps you push or pull the weight through the point of positive failure, for an extra 2–3 reps. In order to achieve maximum in-

Dr. Charles Smith works his legs on the leg press apparatus.

tensity, your training partner must give you only enough assistance to make up the difference between your existing strength level and the 240-pound bench press.

One way to be sure that just enough assistance is being applied in a forced rep situation is for the training partner or spotter to count off the seconds required to push the weight up. If, for example, the weight is being pushed up to lockout in less than 2 seconds, the spotter might be assisting more than he should. Likewise, if it takes longer than 10 seconds, he might not be helping enough.

Forced reps' success is dictated by the recovery rate of a particular muscle group, diet, mental attitude, physical environment and such.

Extracting information from champion bodybuilders the world over, we have learned a few important points about forced reps as they apply to your training mode. First and foremost, this type of training is not for beginners—those who are coming off a layoff from training or those bodybuilders who are plagued with a training injury.

There are three ways that advanced bodybuilders approach their forced rep style of training:

1. doing one forced rep workout per week per body part
2. doing forced reps at every other workout
3. doing three forced rep workouts in succession followed by three nonforced rep workouts

Of the three training situations cited above, the most sensible seems to be the first, especially if you want to avoid overtraining and tendon and ligament injury.

NEGATIVE TRAINING

This method of training offers the physiological benefit of increased strength by conditioning the body to overload stress. Negative reps are the part of the repetition in which you control the lowering of the weight to the starting position. Appropriately, this method of training can be used in a dual capacity with forced reps. After you have completed the forced rep portion of a set, have a training partner or spotter pull the barbell back to arm's length, and then, under your own power, control the descent of the barbell down to the starting position. A properly performed negative rep should take approximately four to five seconds. Generally, when the descent of the negative accelerates to less than four seconds per rep, that is where the set should end. To acquire the most stimulation for the negatives, three reps is a good

Rich Gaspari goes for the final rep on a crossover machine.

cises that would solicit the use of an arm (one-arm dumbbell curls) or leg (one-leg squats), you would use the opposite arm or leg to assist you through the positive portion of the exercise and carry on from there.

This is a normal way of training negative-style as it applies to a conventional set. If you really want to experience the ultimate in negative training, take a poundage that is 20–40 percent over your six-rep maximum and perform four sets of six reps (negative-style only). The first three negative reps should take approximately six seconds each, and the final negative reps should take four seconds per rep. This style of training will require the use of one or more spotters.

Negative rep training requires at least 72 hours of recovery time before another workout of this type can be initiated. So, with this in mind, you might want to try negatives once per week per body part and definitely not more than twice per week.

To determine whether or not you are qualified to pursue negative rep training, follow the guidelines suggested in the information on forced reps.

Unless otherwise indicated, you should not perform negatives or, for that matter, forced reps on more than two sets per exercise, and these two sets should be in the conventional range of 6 reps (no less) to 12 reps (no more).

THE 21 MOVEMENT

This exercise principle was very popular with West Coast bodybuilding champions a few years ago. It goes something like this: choose a poundage you can do for 8–12 reps. Using the standing barbell curl as an example, begin by doing seven half curls from the starting position (thighs)

average to go for, but not more than six per set.

As indicated previously, most negative training requires the use of a spotter. You can, however, perform negatives by cheating the weight (using your own body momentum) up through the positive range of the exercise and then performing your negative rep. This would be applicable to most barbell exercises that require the use of both arms (barbell bench press). If you wanted to do one-limb exer-

John Terilli—note the concentration.

to the navel region. After you have completed these reps, immediately do seven half curls from the navel to the neck, remembering to contract the biceps "hard" at the top. You might want to do a couple of burns every other rep here. Now, without any rest, finish off with seven complete curls. That's the 21 movement.

HEAVY-LIGHT SYSTEM

This is a system that you can apply to one body part or all. It will develop maximum size, power, and shape in a muscle when followed exactly as described. Let's use the deltoids as an example: choose one general exercise from Group No. 1 and one specific exercise from Group No. 2 on the Exercise Selection Chart in Chapter 5.

Let's assume that your selections are the seated press behind the neck from Group No. 1 and the seated side lateral

Lance Dreher works on bench rows.

dumbbell raises from Group No. 2. Begin by performing 2 sets of 6–8 reps (with 84–88 percent of your current 1-rep maximum) in the seated press behind the neck. Rest about three minutes between sets No. 1 and 2. Immediately (without any

rest) after you have completed the second set of the press behind the neck, perform 1 set of 10–12 reps (with approximately 80 percent of your current 1-rep maximum) in the seated side lateral dumbbell raises. Rest one to two minutes and repeat the entire process as described.

After you have completed the entire process a second time, take a five-minute rest. This rest period will give you time to select a new general and specific exercise from Group No. 1 and No. 2 on the Exercise Selection Chart. Now go through another series of the heavy-light system. Upon completion of this series, you will have done 12 sets (4 sets each of two general exercises and 2 sets each of two specific exercises).

While this system of training is more or less a change of pace for the advanced bodybuilder, an intermediate bodybuilder would find this heavy-light system an excellent means by which to specialize in a body part.

Appropriately, an advanced bodybuilder could adapt this method of training for a specialization program simply by performing 4 sets each of three general and 2 sets each of three specific exercises for a combined work load of 18 sets.

SUPERSETS

This is one of the most popular training principles among advanced bodybuilders. There are numerous ways to achieve success with supersets. You can alternate between two exercises for opposing body parts in a nonstop fashion. An example of this is the supine french press for the triceps, which is a pushing muscle, and the Scott barbell preacher curl for the biceps, which is a pulling muscle. Another example is the supine bench press for the

Rich Gaspari works the crossover pulleys for chest.

chest and the lat machine pulldown for the latissimus dorsi muscle in the back.

Generally, when exercises are performed in superset fashion for opposing body parts, one exercise uses a pushing muscle while the other is of a pulling nature. You can come up with many superset exercise combinations of your own in the push-and-pull style if you use the Exercise Selection Chart in Chapter 5, "Structuring a Workout Schedule" and the push and pull chart in Chapter 10, "Muscle Injuries—Causes and Treatment." You can choose from a variety of exercise sequences when planning a superset session that involves a push-pull combination for two opposite body parts. In our first superset example, we selected an exercise for the triceps that is termed a general exercise while the exercise for the biceps was a specific exercise.

PUSHING MUSCLE	PULLING MUSCLE
Triceps	Biceps
a. Supine French Press	b. Scott Barbell Preacher Curl

We could just as easily have picked a specific exercise for the triceps and a general exercise for the biceps. Then again, one general exercise for each of these muscles is not out of the question. Finally, in certain cases it would not be uncommon to select a specific exercise for each opposite muscle and work it in superset fashion.

Another way you can use supersets in your exercise program is by doing two pulling exercises back to back, such as heavy barbell curls and Scott dumbbell curls. Or you could work at doing two pushing exercises together, such as narrow-grip (12-inch) bench press to neck and one-arm dumbbell kickbacks. Since

Clare Furr does some heavy squats—a regular treatment in her leg program.

you will be working the same muscle with two exercises, you will need to take a slight rest of 15–30 seconds between supersets as opposed to no rest (unless absolutely needed) when working opposing body parts in superset fashion. Because of the intensity involved in working two exercises for the same body part, it is our

Mike Christian performs heavy flyes for his chest.

recommendation that you not superset two general exercises.

The most commonly accepted mode of training superset style here is to begin with a general exercise and follow up with a specific exercise (a takeoff from the heavy-light system discussed earlier).

Now if you prefer to begin with a specific exercise and finish with a general exercise, the following principle will be most helpful.

PREEXHAUSTION PRINCIPLE

This unique exercise principle was invented back in the 1960s as a means of working a prime mover muscle with the greatest amount of intensity. It is used by many bodybuilding champions to shock their muscles into new growth.

Preexhaust specifies that if you intend to work a prime mover muscle group (e.g., mid-pecs of the chest) with a generalized exercise (e.g., supine bench press) that not only stresses the prime mover but also the synergistic or helping muscles (in this situation it is the tricep muscles), you should first do a specific exercise (e.g., supine dumbbell flyes) that works the prime mover muscle group exclusively.

Now that the prime mover muscles have been preexhausted by the supine dumbbell flyes, you will get a good workout from the supine bench press, which works both the prime mover and synergistic muscles. Preexhaustion, in other words, gets around the problem of synergistic (and, in some instances, the stabilizer or supporting) muscles tiring before the prime movers and thus rendering a generalized exercise ineffective.

Preexhaustion very effectively maximizes the effect on a prime mover muscle and minimizes the effect on the synergist and stabilizer muscles.

The generally accepted way to preexhaust (using the exercises mentioned above) is to begin your chest routine with a set of supine dumbbell flyes for approximately 10–12 reps and then, without any rest whatsoever (and this is important because if you allow three seconds or more between the exercises your muscles will recover at least 50 percent of their ability to contract and you will lose some

of the effectiveness of the routine), start performing the supine bench press for 6–8 reps.

A slight rest is taken after this exercise, followed by another sequence or two of the above-described technique. This is the basic concept of preexhaustion as it applies to the intermediate bodybuilder.

For those of you advanced bodybuilders who might desire the ultimate experience in preexhaustion training, try this: begin with the supine dumbbell flyes for 10–12 reps. After you have finished these, immediately do another set of these flyes with a poundage that is 10 pounds lighter (per dumbbell), and again after the conclusion of this set, immediately drop off another 10 pounds, and finish off with a final third set.

Immediately begin the supine bench

Joseph Gromlus of Germany shows impressive overall muscular development.

"The Myth" and "The Golden Eagle."

press for six to eight reps to positive failure. Now strip 20 percent of the poundage off the barbell and do as many extra positive reps as you can. When these are done, drop another 20 percent off the barbell and finish off with reps to positive failure. Rest three to five minutes and begin this cycle one final time.

This program is generally adaptable to the bodybuilder who is training alone. If you are fortunate enough to have a training partner, this preexhaustion principle can be expanded as follows.

1. Perform the dumbbell flyes as advised.
2. Beginning with the first set of the supine bench press, go to positive failure as advised. Now have your training partner assist you with some forced reps, then finish off this first set with some negatives.
3. Drop the poundage by 20 percent and follow the directions above.
4. Drop another 20 percent off the barbell and go through your third and final set of positive failure, forced and negative reps.

You have just completed one series. Rest three to five minutes and begin a final series, if you can. On this second series, eliminate the forced and negative reps on each set, doing just the positive failure reps and the 20-percent poundage drops.

A couple of things you should keep in mind about this super-intense method of preexhaustion:

First, if you are going to be utilizing this exercise principle more than twice per week on a body part, you should adhere to the advice given earlier in the chapter about forced reps and negatives by doing these no more than two workout days per week and for only one series.

Secondly, for greatest success, allow no more than three seconds to elapse between the specific and general exercises

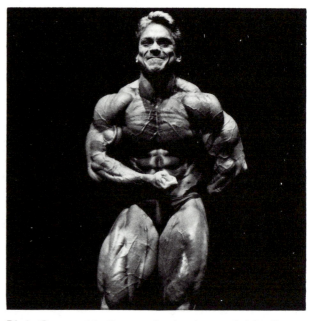

Rich Gaspari is the perfect role model for those who want to achieve Herculean muscularity.

PREEXHAUSTION CHART

BODY PART	SPECIFIC EXERCISE	GENERAL EXERCISE
Thighs	Leg Extensions	Olympic-style Squat
Trapezius	Barbell or Dumbbell Shrugs	Power Cleans or Wide-Grip Upright Rowing
Latissimus	Barbell Decline Pullovers	Lat Pulldowns
Middle Back	Bent-forward (90-degree) Dumbbell Lateral to Side	Barbell Bent-over Rows
Spinae Erectors	Prone Hyperextensions (30-inch-high bench)	Stiff-Legged Deadlift
Upper Pecs	Incline (35-to 45-degree) Dumbbell Flyes	Incline Barbell Press
Mid-Pecs	Supine Dumbbell Flyes	Supine Bench Press
Low Pecs	Decline Dumbbell Flyes	Decline Barbell Press
Deltoids	Dumbbell Side Lateral Raise	Press Behind Neck
Biceps	Scott Barbell Curl	Regular-Grip (palms-facing) Chinups
Triceps	Triceps Pushdowns	Parallel Bar Dips
Abs	Crunches	Incline (45-degree) Situps
Forearms	Barbell Palms-down Wrist Curl	Barbell Reverse Curl
Calf	Seated Calf Raise	Standing Calf Machine

and the sets within each type of exercise. It is therefore very important that you set up the appropriate poundages you plan to use ahead of time.

TRISETS

This method of training is very similar to supersets as it applies to doing exercises back to back for the same muscle. The noted difference is that you will perform *three* exercises back to back.

A good illustration of doing three exercises back to back for the deltoids is to begin with the seated press behind the neck for 6–8 reps, then do standing side dumbbell lateral raises for 10–12 reps, and finally finish off with bent-over dumbbell lateral raises for 10 reps or so.

Rest approximately one or two minutes and begin the cycle a second time. The deltoid exercises represent one generalized movement that works the overall delt followed by two specific movements that attack the medial and posterior segments of the deltoid respectively.

If you decide that you want to blitz the posterior segment of the delt only in a triset, you pick out three specific exercises for this area and do them in the manner described.

Interestingly, the triset that is represented above for the deltoid—one generalized movement followed by two specific movements—can be changed in order of performance in a double preexhaustion sequence. Deltoids: side dumbbell lateral raise, plus seated press behind the neck, plus bent-over dumbbell lateral raise. As an option, you could go with side dumbbell lateral raise, plus seated press behind the neck, plus side dumbbell lateral raise again.

Vera Bendel is West Germany's answer to Bev Francis.

GIANT SETS

Giant sets are an extension of supersets and trisets in which you do anywhere from four to six exercises for either one particular body part or two opposite body parts. It is very important that you do the exercises in sequence, one right after the other, without any rest between (as would normally be the case if you were doing straight sets). Only when you have completed the last exercise in the sequence can you take a much needed rest of one to two minutes before beginning a second or third giant set sequence, as the case may be.

Rather than give you some type of exhaustive listing of the routines you might use in giant sets, we think you will get a pretty good idea of ways to use the giant set by simply referring to the routines listed in Chapter 5, "Body Part Specialization." For instance, abdominal programs no. 1 (do not include the one-half-mile jog as part of the giant set) and no. 2 are easily adapted to giant set form, as are many other listings throughout the chapter.

When training his calves, Sergio Oliva works barefooted to get the greatest range of movement possible.

There are many ways to vary your approach to performing giant sets, including the following.

1. A general exercise followed by a specific exercise. In other words, your first, third, and fifth exercises are the heavier size- and power-building movements, while the second, fourth, and sixth are the lighter isolation and shaping movements.

2. Reverse the order of the above procedure and you can do a combined preexhaustion giant set. Here's how:

Chest Giant Set

1. Supine Dumbbell Flyes
2. Supine Barbell Bench Press
3. 35-degree Incline Dumbbell Flyes
4. 35-degree Incline Barbell Bench Press
5. Decline Dumbbell Flyes
6. Decline Barbell Bench Press

Notice that exercises 1 and 2 work the mid-pecs, while 3 and 4 hit the clavicular or high pec region and 5 and 6 finish off the lower pecs.

A preexhaust giant set for the total back might look like this . . .

Rich Gaspari helps John Brown with incline flyes.

Corinna Everson looks great from any angle.

Back Giant Set

1. Bent-forward (90-degrees) Dumbbell Lateral Raises
2. Barbell Bent-over Rows
3. Barbell Decline Pullovers
4. Lat Pulldowns
5. Prone Hyperextensions
6. Stiff-legged Deadlift

Exercises 1 and 2 work the middle lat and rhomboids, while 3 and 4 work the upper/outer lat and 5 and 6 work the spinae erectors. Options for training the back could include replacing exercises 1 and 2 with barbell shrugs and power cleans, which work the trapezius rather than the middle lat, etc.

3. Remember the double preexhaustion sequence (one specific exercise followed by a general and finished up with a specific) mentioned in the information on trisets? Instead of working one particular body part, why not work opposing parts (push and pull) in a giant set double preexhaust manner? Using the above chest and back examples, simply arrange the sequence so that chest exercises 1, 2, and 3 (or 4, 5, and 6) are followed by back exercises 1, 2, and 3 (or 4, 5, and 6). Other body groupings that lend themselves to giant set double preexhaustion are the biceps/triceps, spinae erectors/abs, delts/traps, quads/hamstrings.

4. Do giant sets with specific exercises only (less preexhaustion techniques). This method is quite appropriate for the female bodybuilder who wishes to add extra shape to a muscle.

You can perform four to six specific exercises for one particular body part or two to three specific exercises each for two opposite body parts. This instruction, with regard to the number of exercises you will perform in a giant set, does vary

---

PYRAMID TRAINING EXAMPLE

EXERCISE	SETS/REPS		PERCENTAGE OF ONE-REP MAXIMUM
Heavy Barbell Curls	2	12	80
	2	6	84
	2	4	88
	2	2	92

This is a good example of a general exercise. If you decide to use this method with a specific exercise, you will want to begin your repetition scheme slightly higher than the suggested maximum of 12 reps. Here is how standing dumbbell side laterals for the delts might be done in pyramid style.

EXAMPLE

EXERCISE	SETS/REPS		PERCENTAGE OF ONE-REP MAXIMUM
Dumbbell Side Laterals	2	14	68
	2	12	72
	2	10	76
	2	8	80

Unless otherwise indicated, the requirements for general and specific exercises should always meet the demands of the Holistic Training Guide in Chapter 2.

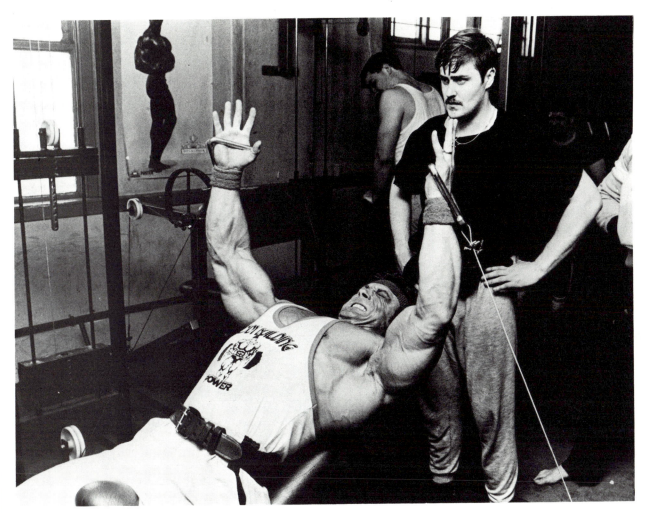

Frank Richards performs cable flyes.

somewhat from that given in Chapter 4, "Structuring a Workout Schedule."

If you're an intermediate bodybuilder, you should use the minimum amount of exercises listed above and for only two cycles of the giant set for one particular body part or four cycles for a giant set consisting of two body parts. If you're an advanced bodybuilder, you should use the maximum number of exercises and for the same number of cycles as the intermediate bodybuilder.

5. For purposes of specialization, the intermediate bodybuilder would do well to use five exercises per giant set for a total of three cycles, while the advanced bodybuilder will find it appropriate to perform six exercises and four cycles.

In giant set specialization you should specialize in only one body part at a time and leave plenty of time for rest in order for the muscle to recover properly.

PYRAMID TRAINING

For this mode of training, you add poundage and decrease the repetition scheme in each succeeding set.

This is a good example of a general exercise. If you decide to use this method with a specific exercise, you will want to begin your repetition scheme slightly higher than the suggested maximum of 12 reps. Here is how standing dumbbell side laterals for the delts might be done in pyramid style.

Unless otherwise indicated, the requirements for general and specific exercises should always meet the demands of the Holistic Training Guide in Chapter 2.

UP-AND-DOWN-THE-RACK SYSTEM

This system of training is a favorite to this day of two-time Olympia winner Larry Scott, and it goes like this:

For the purpose of illustration, let's use the Dumbbell Overhead Press. Begin with a pair of dumbbells that you can press overhead for six solid reps. Now, after you have finished off these reps, go immediately to another, progressively heavier set of dumbbells and press these overhead. Continue in this manner until you have reached a poundage that will allow you to complete only three maximum reps.

That's it for going up the rack for this particular exercise. Going down the rack is simply the reverse of the previous procedure and is usually done immediately following up the rack, for two or three sets.

It is really important that you minimize your rest time between sets. The only way you can do that is to have your dumbbells set up ahead of time so that you can go rapidly from one set to another as instructed.

Keep in mind that on general exercises you will not go below three reps, and on specific exercises not below eight reps on a final set in the up-the-rack system.

Ed Kawak shows massive muscularity.

Have you ever wondered how Larry Scott built up his incredible deltoids? He used a shoulder-blasting routine incorporating the up-and-down-the-rack system. He would do dumbbell overhead presses, followed by dumbbell bent-over lateral raises, and finally standing side dumbbell lateral raises. He would do maybe 6–10 sets per series and about 6 reps on the press, 8–10 reps on the lateral raises per set. He would work his way up and down the rack with no rest between sets and very little rest between exercise series.

Most of the time, Larry would use dumbbells rather than barbells in his shoulder training. Why? Because he feels that barbells aggravate the shoulder region because of the improper torque that is applied to the shoulder joint. He feels that "dumbbells are good because you can

Berry DeMay shows why he is Holland's best.

move the elbows in an arc, and that is the way the deltoids want to move."

THE MULTIPOUNDAGE PRINCIPLE

This training principle is known by three other names: *strip sets*, *descending sets*, and *triple dropping sets*. For the purpose of illustration, we will use the regular bent-knee deadlift. To begin, warm up with one or two sets of deadlifts, using two-thirds of your current 1-rep maximum poundage. Perform 8–10 reps on these warm-up sets. Rest only a minute or so between these sets. Now increase the poundage to near your current maximum double. This is usually 4 or 5 percent less than your 1-rep maximum. Perform 2 reps with this poundage. Now immediately strip a barbell plate off each side of the bar and perform as many reps as you can with

this poundage. Continue in this fashion (performing the reps and stripping the poundage) until you have accumulated a total of 25–32 reps for this particular exercise.

Guidelines

1. This system of training is to be used on general exercises only.

2. To begin with, you will have to experiment to find the appropriate poundage decreases so that you can load your barbell with the right plates for displacement after each rep.

3. Basically, the poundage decreases should be approximately 10 pounds off each side of the bar on exercises such as Olympic squats, leg presses, power squats, and various deadlifts. Five pounds off each side of the bar seems to work efficiently for all other general exercises.

4. To make this system work at maximum intensity, you must not allow more than three to five seconds to elapse when removing the weight for the next series of reps. We would recommend that a training partner help you with this. This method works particularly well with selectorized equipment, where you only have to change a pin to alter the resistance.

5. You may wonder whether the suggested 25–32 repetitions constitute one set. The answer to this question is no. Each time you reduce the poundage on the barbell to begin with more additional reps, you are doing another set. For example, after your warm-up of two sets in the regular bent-knee deadlift you would go to:

REGULAR BENT-KNEE DEADLIFTS

POUNDS	×	REPS
400	×	2
380	×	4
360	×	6
340	×	8
320	×	10

Hypothetically speaking, you will be performing five or so sets. You must realize that these sets, reps, and poundages will vary somewhat according to your muscular and cardiovascular endurance.

The most notable advantage of the multipoundage principle is the use of near-maximum poundages on each and every set. By adhering to little more than three seconds of rest between the poundage decreases, the overall intensity of the exercise remains quite high. The only slight disadvantage might be the problem of cardiovascular exhaustion, which tends to become evident during the fourth set and carries through the fifth set. This is only a minor problem and can be defeated by adapting more of a mental toughness in your approach to training.

REST PAUSE TRAINING

This method of training and its variations combine brief amounts of rest with selected poundage and repetition schemes in a particular set to apply a blowtorch intensity to the muscle. Let's take a look at the methods of rest pause training.

What a back—none better than Mike Christian's.

Lee Haney concludes his amazing routine at the '85 Olympia.

Method 1

On this method, use 75–80 percent of your current maximum poundage for the number of reps you plan to do for a normal set of an exercise. For example, if you can perform the press behind the neck with 200 pounds for 10 reps, take approximately 150–160 pounds and begin your program in the following manner. Perform 10 reps, then rest 10 seconds, then do 9 reps, then rest 10 seconds. Continue in this manner until you are down to 1 rep. Depending on your stamina, you may be able to do more than 1 rep. Go to failure on this final set until you can't even budge the barbell.

Method 2

Begin by warming up with 60 percent of your current 6-rep maximum, for 8–10 reps. Now increase the poundage that will allow you to perform 6 solid hard-work reps. Perform these 6 reps and then rest for 60 seconds. Continue in this manner for a total of 10 sets per individual exercise. If at any point during the 10 sets your reps drop to a count of 5, decrease the poundage only enough to ensure performing the basic 6-rep pattern.

Method 3

This is another method of rest pause training that suggests the use of a 10-set pattern. Warm up with 60 percent of your current maximum for the number of reps you plan to perform.

Let's assume that you want to acquire some power in your 35-degree incline bench press. Currently, your best incline bench press might be 300 pounds for five reps. (Your best maximum single attempt will be approximately 16–21 percent more than this. This figures out to be 348 pounds at 16 percent or 363 pounds at 21 percent, based on the 300 pounds for five reps. Based on a four-rep maximum, you can expect to do 14–16 percent more and a triple or three-rep max produces 10–13 percent more poundage for a single attempt.)

Begin your first set of 35-degree incline bench presses with 80 percent of your five-rep poundage. You are looking at 240 pounds for the first set. Now rest one minute between succeeding sets.

During each of these rest periods, up to the fifth set, you will add 5 percent to the barbell until you are using 100 percent of your five-rep maximum for the fifth and sixth.

After these two sets are completed, you will begin to decrease the poundage by 5 percent on each of the final 4 sets of the 10-set maximum.

35-DEGREE INCLINE BENCH PRESS

300 POUNDS × 5 reps

SETS	REPS	POUNDAGE	PERCENTAGE
1	5	240	80
2	5	255	85
3	5	270	90
4	5	285	95
5	5	300	100
6	5	300	100
7	5	285	95
8	5	270	90
9	5	255	85
10	5	240	80

Marjo Selin performs hack squats.

To give you a better idea of how this system works, here's a full outline of it.

On the fifth and sixth sets you may not be able to do the prescribed five reps per set. This is a result of the minimal rest pauses of one minute between sets as compared to the conventional requirement of resting three to eight minutes between sets.

Do whatever you can in this respect until you are able to perform 5 reps on each and every set, then upgrade your poundage-percentage (based on a new 5-rep maximum) scale and begin a new cycle of the 10-set rest pause.

You might also try utilizing the one-minute rest period by incorporating a su-

Muscular Sue Ann McKean.

Juliette Bergman shows remarkable
muscularity and symmetry.

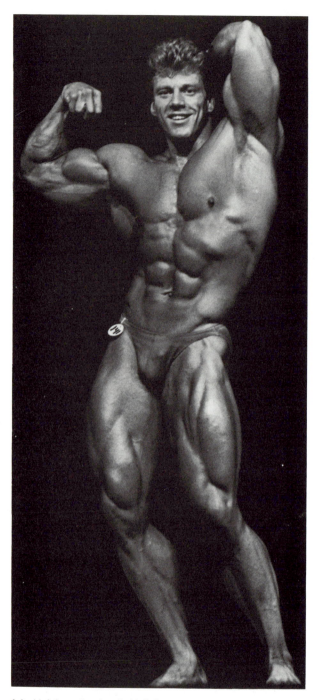

Matt Mendenhall, U.S.A.

3–5 for power, 6–8 for size and strength, and 8–12 for strength/endurance.

As we have mentioned time and again throughout this book, specific exercises are best accomplished with rep patterns of between 8 and 12.

Method 4: Six Sets of 10 Reps

Find a poundage you can do 10 reps with. Now add 10 percent more weight to the barbell. You will do 10 reps on each set, but the secret to accomplishing this task is the length of the rest periods. Set 1 ends, and you will take a 30-second rest. Now, on each additional set, add 15 seconds to your rest periods. After the second set you will rest 45 seconds; after the third set, 60 seconds; after the fourth set, 1¼ minutes; after the fifth set, 1½ minutes, etc.

When you get to the point where you can do all six sets rather easily for 10 reps, add more poundage.

Method 5

This rest pause method follows the same six-set/10-rep requirement, but with a slight twist. Find a poundage you can do 10 reps with. Now decrease this poundage by 5 percent. Your rest intervals between sets are a firm 30 seconds—no more, no less. The first set you will probably accomplish 9–10 reps. The second set you may only accomplish 7–8 reps. The reps may become fewer and fewer as you finish up your sixth and final set. When you get to the point where you are doing 10 reps rather easily on all six sets, it is time to add more poundage to the barbell.

THE JETTISON TECHNIQUE

This remarkable technique is one of the newer and most effective muscle-building techniques around today. Here's a five-

perset pattern for an opposite body part.

You can employ different rep patterns based on your particular goals at the time. On general exercises you can use reps of

step system outlining how the technique is performed.

1. Find the total weight on a barbell or dumbbell (after a good warm-up) that will permit you to perform 16 reps in the exercise of your choice. We'll use the upright rowing exercise for the deltoids as an example.

2. Now take one-third of this weight off the bar, whether it be a barbell or a dumbbell. Put this poundage aside for a moment and secure the remaining poundage on the bar with regular collars. Lock the remaining one-third poundage onto the outside of the regular collars with some type of quick-release collars (the Joe Weider EZ-On/EZ-Off collars are excellent for this purpose) so that you can remove the one-third poundage quickly when instructed to do so.

3. Next take a set of five round rubber expander cables and find out how many cables you will need to provide resistance for a total of 16 reps in the barbell-related exercise you have chosen. In this case you will perform the upright rows with the round rubber expander cable set.

Note: Two sets of the five round rubber expander cable sets will be required when performing any arm or shoulder movement that would call for using a barbell or two dumbbells. Any singular one-arm movement you might choose for the arms and shoulders would naturally require only one expander set.

4. You have now determined from step 1 the proper poundage that is necessary to perform 16 reps in the upright-rowing exercise. Also, step 3 has afforded you the opportunity of knowing precisely

JETTISON TECHNIQUE

A = 2/3 poundage
B = 1/3 poundage
C = round rubber expander cable sets
GET SET
Begin the upright rowing exercise as instructed in step 5 and go to *momentary failure*. Now jettison the expander sets and begin the exercise as depicted in illustration No. 2.

how many rubber expander cables you will need in order to perform 16 reps in the upright rows with the round rubber expander cable set.

Theoretically, you should not be able to do more than 8 reps with the combined resistances of the weights and the rubber expander cables. You must realize, though, that each person is different in terms of strength potential, so the suggested repetition scheme of 8 could be as low as 6 or as high as 10 reps.

5. *Get Set*: Grab the rubber expander cable handles. Next, grab the barbell or dumbbell handles and begin performing upright rows with the combined resistance of the two pieces of exercise apparatus. Perform as many reps as you can until you are fatigued to the point of momentary failure. Immediately jettison (abandon or reject) the expander cable handles. Continue the exercise motion. When you can't perform another repetition, quickly release the one-third poundage (step 2)

from the barbell or dumbbells and continue the upright rows with this weight until you can no longer do another rep.

The five steps constitute one sequence of the jettison technique. Perform a total of three sequences, resting only 45–60 seconds between sequences, if you are an intermediate or advanced bodybuilder. Bodybuilding beginners would be better off saving this very advanced technique until they come to the intermediate stage of bodybuilding, and then this technique is a very good method by which to blast past a training plateau or sticking point in a training routine.

Gradually, over a period of workouts, increase your training intensity by working up to 12–14 reps in the first part of the sequence, where both the weight and the expander cables are used as a combined resistance. At this time you will add enough weight and additional cables to drop you back to a base of 8 reps, as noted in step 4. Follow through with step 5!

Perform the upright rows with the poundages of A and B and to *momentary failure*. Now jettison poundage B.

The exercises that are the most functional from the standpoint of the existing stretching capacity and range of movement of the rubber expanders are the various curling movements for the biceps, reverse curling for the forearms, and upright rows and lateral raises for the deltoids. Overhead-type exercises, such as standing presses and tricep extensions, present a problem in that most expander sets are not long enough to allow for the range of movement needed. The solution to this problem is to replace the original expander cables with surgical rubber tubing that has been cut to the proper length (and tied to the cable handles), which will allow you to perform any overhead exercise movement from a standing position.

The jettison technique should be used only on one exercise for a body part and as a last exercise.

Continue the upright rows with this final poundage and to *momentary failure*. This constitutes one sequence of the jettison technique.

Bob Paris of California.

7
THE WISDOM BEHIND PHASE TRAINING

Phase training is the master plan that many of the world's strongest and best-developed men and women use to achieve their short- and long-term goals for acquiring superhuman strength or molding a top physique.

Phase training is commonly known in the bodybuilding community as cycle training. Cycle training is the periodic alteration of training loads and methods as it applies to stimulating the ultimate in size and strength.

Successful phase training requires certain exercises, specific sets and reps, and corresponding poundage percentages be performed periodically a minimum of three weeks in order to begin stimulating a muscle to its maximum.

If you were to review your training (as you should) on a month-to-month basis, you would more than likely find some occasional plateaus or decreases in performance level as your body reacts to a particular exercise or in some cases a number of exercises.

There are numerous ways in which this can occur, but two that we consider most important are as follows.

First, the central nervous system (CNS), the mind, and the muscles work together as a unit in order to produce the necessary and natural chemical changes in the body. It is these changes that create and develop a bodybuilder's strength, endurance, and visible changes in physical development.

However, just as soon as these changes are made, the central nervous system and the muscles adapt or adjust to the stress that was placed on them. When this happens, there will usually be a temporary cessation of continued gains. For example, you might be encountering a plateau in which you can't do more than 300 pounds in the bench press for eight reps. If this happens in just one particular workout, it probably is not a plateau. A plateau is generally evident when you have done three or more particular workouts using this exercise and there has

Russ Testo forces out one more rep.

been no marked response in either the poundage or repetition gains.

At this point it should be understood that the plateau in the performance level of the exercise cited above is a normal adjustment that the central nervous system and the muscles make to a particular method of training overload.

Another way in which a training plateau can occur is when training loads are intensified, but not enough recovery time is given to the muscles. This error in training will not allow the body to regain previously established energy levels for the next scheduled workout session. This is the classic case of the bodybuilder who is overtraining the body.

Generally, more recovery time between workouts is necessary on larger body parts than on smaller body parts. Larger body parts such as the thighs and the lower back need about five days of rest between workouts when performing general exercises like conventional squats and deadlifts. The chest needs three to four days of rest when general bench press movements are employed. The recovery demands on the above body parts

	MON	TUES	WED	THUR	FRI	SAT	SUN
Week No. 1	Squat & Deadlift	Bench Press			Bench Press	Deadlift & Squat	
2		Bench Press		Squat	Bench Press		
3	Bench Press	Squat & Deadlift				Bench Press	Deadlift & Squat
4			Bench Press		Squat	Bench Press	
5		Bench Press	Squat & Deadlift			Bench Press	
6	Deadlift & Squat	Bench Press			Bench Press	Squat	
7		Bench Press		Deadlift & Squat		Bench Press	
8		Squat & Deadlift	Bench Press			Bench Press	Squat
9		Bench Press			Deadlift & Squat	Bench Press	
10		Bench Press	Squat & Deadlift		Bench Press		
11	Squat	Bench Press			Bench Press	Squat & Deadlift	
12	Bench Press			Deadlift & Squat	Bench Press		

The curl attack! Carolyn Cheshire gets into it.

are affected by the following factors:

1. Many of the same muscles are used interchangeably on the squatting and deadlifting exercise, so for the most efficient and speedy recovery, these exercises should be done one after the other on the same workout day.

2. Because of the tremendous depletion of the body's energy sources from the above squat and deadlift workout, you should schedule your bench press exercise on a day prior to or a day after the above workout, not on the same day.

Deltoid or shoulder strength or energy is depleted somewhat from doing a deadlift workout, and you need this strength for synergistic and stabilizer functions in the bench press. If you do your squat/deadlift exercises during the morning, the bench press should be done on the following day, but during the evening if possible. This should allow you plenty of time to recover from any incurred stiffness from the previous workout day.

Because of the slight difference in the number of rest days required for the above exercises, the following chart should make it convenient for you to plan your training around these exercises. The method of training depicted in the chart is not the final word in training procedures, though it is one of the best ones from which to choose, especially if adequate recovery time between workouts is important to you.

Lee Haney trains his delts with the press behind the neck exercise as part of his phase-training routine.

You might have noticed that deadlifts and squats (or vice versa) are done together twice in a row, but then on every third workout the deadlifts are eliminated for eight to nine days. This is because many strength experts feel that the lower back does not recover quite as quickly as the legs, and skipping the third workout deadlift situation helps recovery time.

Since every bodybuilder is unique, you might experience just the opposite

effect, so here you will have to adjust the program to meet your needs.

3. You should be using training poundages in excess of an 84- to 88-percent one-rep maximum.

Smaller body parts such as the shoulders, biceps, triceps, and lats require two to three days of recovery time between workouts, while the forearms, abdominals, and calves need only two or fewer days of recovery time (due to the fact that these body parts are predominately red-fiber endurance slow-twitch muscles and don't demand as much energy during a workout; and hence they don't need as much time to recover).

TRAINING FREQUENCY PROBLEMS

Muscle Exhaustion

As we mentioned earlier, many of the same muscles are used in exercises for different body parts. To illustrate this point, let's suppose that you begin your upper body workout with a pressing movement to the pecs (probably the bench press). No problem yet, but as you get further into your workouts you will more than likely do some type of pressing movements for your frontal deltoids.

Now a problem begins to become evident. You notice that upon commencement of the overhead press your strength is suffering somewhat. This is because the deltoids and triceps muscles had been exhausted somewhat from the earlier bench press movement for the pecs. As you continue with your workout, the problem is magnified as you finish off your routine with some lying french presses for the triceps.

Your triceps are so fatigued from the

Robby Robinson and Tony Pearson go at it with impressive "most musculars."

Janet Tech, U.S.A., shows good form on a lat pull.

• If you are doing a push-pull split training routine where you must do all your pressing-type exercises in the same workout, you might schedule your routine so that you work chest and then deltoids and finish off with triceps. The next time these body parts are to be worked, go with delts/chest/triceps or triceps/chest/delts, but again this must be based on your training objectives.

Recovery Time

We mentioned earlier the amount of recovery time that is necessary for the performance of squats, benches, and deadlifts, based on training poundages in excess of 84–88 percent of your one-rep current maximum in the lift. These types of training poundages would suggest that you are training for an upcoming powerlifting competition. If you would like to do these particular exercises and utilize the same recovery time table as for the smaller body parts (shoulders, biceps, triceps, and lats), you probably should reduce your training poundages to under 84 percent of your one-rep maximum as it applies to the general exercise movements. It takes more time to recover from training loads in excess of 84 percent of your maximum than it does at a lesser percentage.

The recovery timetable doesn't change dramatically for the smaller body parts when general exercises are done with training loads in excess of 84 percent simply because the energy requirements for these body parts are so much lower (less oxygen, less lactic acid buildup) than for the larger body parts that use squat, bench press, and deadlift types of movements.

Summed up, though, it is these big three exercises that contribute most to the response in the muscles of the body, both directly and indirectly.

previous pressing movements for the other body parts that you just aren't able to do as many reps or sets, and not nearly as much poundage, as you could before these other two exercises. There are some solutions to these problems, but always remember that they must be based on your training objectives.

Solutions

• Don't do your pressing exercises for different body parts one after the other. It is better to do a pressing movement for one body part, then go on to another body part in which you can do a curling-type movement, then go on to another body part pressing movement, etc.

Other Problems

Other problems you're likely to encounter include how to determine the number of exercises to do per body part and the numbers of reps and sets. The solutions to these problems are discussed in Chapter 2, "The Science of Reps and Sets."

Other factors such as your existing general fitness level (improved by aerobic training) and nutritional habits will shorten recovery time on heavy workouts. After a workout you should feel comfortably tired. The following day you should feel energetic and the muscles should feel firm (toned) and hard when flexed.

GOALS OF PHASE TRAINING

If it is your desire to prevent the leveling off of bodybuilding gains, you must use various methods of training overloads that will create a proper balance between the capacity of the central nervous sytem and that of the muscles to respond to the stress of the training method used.

Instinctive training comes into play here. This is basically the performance of exercise based on individual interpretation and feel. You must become aware of what your body is telling you.

This is done in part by the brain, which receives signals from the nerve endings and other receptors in the body. It can indicate to you the response of the various amounts of muscle contraction and stretching and the pressure in the muscle from the sets and reps you are doing. It can also be instrumental in helping you not to overtrain, because when you understand how your body reacts to training stimulus, you will know when you have done enough reps, sets, and exer-

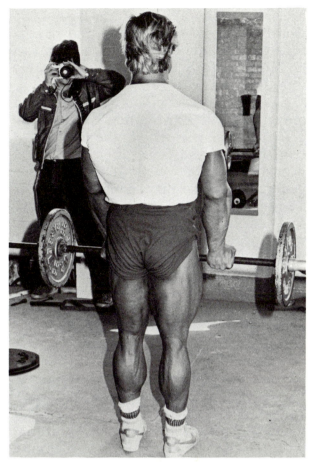

Who Else? The amazing Tom Platz.

cises in a workout. It usually takes six months to a year of consistent training to begin understanding how your body reacts to progressive weight training.

If it is your desire to produce continued gains time and time again with very little problem of training plateaus or general overtraining, then phase training is your answer. Many of the top physique and strength champions learned a while ago that the body cannot tolerate peak performance training for more than a very short time.

As a means to combat this problem, these champions begin employing light, medium, and heavy training loads in a variety of ways throughout the year. We are going to share with you the best of two worlds, that of bodybuilding and power-lifting, regarding how phase training can be incorporated successfully into your existing training program.

Before we begin detailing this method of training, you should know that it is the general consensus among the majority of bodybuilders and powerlifters the world over that a particular phase of training is generally effective up to a maximum of 8–12 weeks on high-volume/low-intensity and medium-volume/medium-intensity training, while the low-volume/high-intensity overloads are generally effective from as little as five and up to a maximum of eight weeks of training.

In order to determine which of the above methods of phase training to begin with, you must establish some type of goal. If you are coming off a layoff (for the purpose of just resting the body or to recover from illness or possibly an injury), you should consider the advantages of beginning your first phase of training with some high-volume/low-intensity workouts for an 8- to 12-week period.

This is basically the performance of endurance training (use 60–78 percent of one rep maximum), where you begin training with lighter poundages and more sets and reps. In this phase of your training the mental attitude is the most important consideration and not necessarily the amount of poundage on the bar. The weight must feel light until your enthusiasm for training builds up again.

To prevent muscle injury and severe muscle soreness, especially after a layoff, you must never attempt to begin training with a previously established workout intensity.

After this phase of training is completed to your satisfaction, you might begin your next training phase with medium-volume/medium-intensity workouts

Joseph Gromlus of Germany.

for 8–12 weeks. This phase will bring you back to a previously established training level of strength/endurance (80 percent of one-rep maximum).

Finally, to bring your strength/size (80–84 percent of one-rep maximum), use a six- to eight-week cycle. Then finish off with five or six weeks of building up to maximum power (88–92 percent of one-rep maximum). Both of these training phases are termed *lower-volume/high-intensity* and are applicable only to general exercises.

Note:
- *Endurance* = high volume/low intensity
- *Strength/Endurance* = medium volume/high intensity
- *Strength/Size* = low volume/high intensity
- *Power* = low volume/high intensity

Refer to the holistic training guide in Chapter 2, "The Science of Reps and Sets," for other necessary information.

Specific (isolating or shaping) exercises are rather limited in the scope of repetition variance during the final two training phases just presented. There are other ways to avoid training plateaus on these exercises during times like this, and we suggest you read over Chapters 3 and 6, "Training Mechanics—Muscle Overloading," and "Optimum Muscle Blasting," for some really good ideas on creating continued muscle stimuli.

We have met very few bodybuilders who were *not* interested in developing extra strength for future workouts. Here is a proven phase of training that will help you develop a good measure of superhuman strength.

POWER TRAINING ROUTINE

MONDAY

EXERCISE	SETS		REPS	PERCENTAGES
Conventional Deadlifts	1	×	10	50
Rest 4 - 5 minutes between sets.	1	×	8	70
Concentrate on form and keep shoulders pulled	1	×	3	80
back on each rep.	1	×	3	90
	3	×	3	80
Barbell High Pulls. Rest 3 minutes between sets: Explode on the pull, then lower the weight rather slowly.	3	×	6	60
Parallel Bar Dips. Rest 3 - 4 minutes between sets. Explode from the low	1	×	10	30
dead-stop position. Except for the set to failure, this	1	×	6	50
exercise is done with extra poundage.	3	×	3	80
Body-Weight-Only Dips	1	×	failure	

TUESDAY AND THURSDAY

Midsection and Neck Work
Do 20 - 30 minutes' worth on these—your choice.

WEDNESDAY

High-Bar Full Squats
Use the same set, rep, and percentage scale as for the deadlift.

	SETS		REPS	
Body-Weight-Only Squat Jumps	2	×	failure	
Barbell Curls (slight cheat)	5	×	5	

Rest 2 minutes between sets on these last two exercises.

FRIDAY

Barbell Bench Press
Use the same set, rep, and percentage scale as for the deadlift and squat.

Chinups/Pullups
Use the same set, rep, and percentage scale as for the parallel bar dip.

One workout, do this exercise with your palms facing you (chinup) and use a narrow 3-inch grip. Then the next workout, do it with palms facing away (pullup). Use a shoulder-width or wider grip.

SATURDAY AND SUNDAY

Complete rest.

EVERY THIRD WEEK ONLY

After the 1 × 3 for 90 percent (conventional deadlift, high bar squat, and bench press) use the following set, rep, and percentage scale.	1	×	3	90
Then do four single attempts beyond this,	1	×	2	95
then finish off with	3	×	3	80

Rest 5 - 7 minutes between single attempts. If for some reason you decided that you might like to enter a powerlift meet, use the following information.

THREE WEEKS PRIOR TO THE CONTEST

Your set, rep, and percentage scales change on these exercises.

Barbell High Pulls	2	×	6	60
Parallel Bar Dips	3	×	6	50
Body-Weight-Only Squat Jumps	2	×	failure	
Barbell Curls (slight cheat)	3	×	7	
Chinups/Pullups	4	×	6	50

Deadlifts, High-Bar Full Squats, and Barbell Bench Presses

During this 3 weeks prior to the powerlift meet, do this sequence on each of the three above lifts.

	SETS		REPS	PERCENTAGES
	1	×	20	30
Rest 2 minutes	1	×	10	50
Rest 2 minutes	1	×	8	60
Rest 3 minutes	1	×	3	70
Rest 5 minutes	1	×	3	90
Rest 5 minutes	1	×	1	95

Then do three more single attempts in 5-pound increments, with a 5-minute rest between attempts.

If you have an abundance of energy, do 1 - 3 more single attempts this way to break your previous record. Then finish off with:

Rest 5 Minutes ....　　1　　×　　15　　15

Tips

Always warm up properly before beginning the scheduled day's workout. The approximate percentages of poundages to be lifted are based on your current best maximum single attempt in the exercise you are doing.

On the deadlifts, parallel bar dips, high-bar full squats, chinups/pullups, and barbell bench press, try to add 10 pounds per week to each set; if not possible, don't settle for anything less than 5 pounds.

Franco Columbu at the World's outdoor gym shows the lean muscularity that made him a champion.

8
A TREASURY OF BODYBUILDING SECRETS

Over the years, we've seen virtually all of the "quick gain" training techniques, most of which don't stay around for very long and eventually fade away. Yet there are other training tips which survive the test of time and provide the added advantage for those in their quest for ultimate musculature.

In this chapter we hope to solve some of the most common training problems (particularly in thigh training) and offer training tips for a variety of bodyparts. We provide these tips in the hope that they just may push past a growth plateau and into a new world of muscular development.

THIGHS

The barbell squat and its variations should always be included in the basic structure of a weight training program.

There are, however, some squatting problems that you should be aware of.

Squatting Problems

Injuries to the Ligaments and Tendons Surrounding the Knee

1. Lack of flexibility in the muscles and tendons surrounding the quads, hamstrings, and calves.
2. Using more poundage than you are accustomed to may force you down farther in the bottom (low) position of the squat, which puts abnormal stress on the ligaments and tendons.
3. Squatting down in an uncontrolled manner where you basically drop quickly through the descending phase of the movement and then literally rebound to the starting position.

Solutions
1. To overcome the lack of flexibility in the muscles of the quads, hamstrings,

Robby Robinson—an all-time great.

for that matter) properly and in strict form. Doing strict full-range-of-movement exercises like squats with a poundage you can control on each and every rep will subject the muscle to more training intensity than will a weight that is obviously too heavy.

Increased Glute or Buttocks Size from Squatting Movements
The gluteus or buttocks, like any other skeletal muscle, will increase somewhat in size, either directly or indirectly, from exercise stimulation. Generally, the area will grow in proportion to other muscles in the body, but there is a slight chance that you may have a predetermined genetic problem in which this muscle is in fact larger in proportion to other surrounding muscles. It is possible that you could add to your problems by going lower than parallel in your squats. What happens here is that the glutes, being stronger than the thighs, involve themselves strongly in the recovery part of the movement. As a result, the glutes are in a sense receiving more exercise stimuli than the quads and hamstrings.

Solutions Squat only to the parallel position of the squatting movement. This will help overcome to a degree maximum use of the glutes. It is also an acceptable way to prevent ligament and tendon injury in the knees.

Another factor you must consider is that your glutes may appear to be larger than normal due to lack of development in the hamstrings or thigh biceps. If this is the case, do some priority training for the thigh biceps.

Sacroiliac Dislocation and/or Strain from Squatting Sacroiliac dislocation or strain can be caused by carrying the barbell too high on the back of your neck, which in turn puts massive pressure on

and calves, it is important that you do some stretching prior to squatting.
2. Always use a poundage that is within your present level of strength.
3. Perform your squats (and all exercises,

the spine. Also, failure to maintain an upright posture during the squatting movement can contribute to a serious back injury.

What happens here is that you allow the back to hump. This, combined with the other squatting problems mentioned above, causes the back sides of the discs on the spine to open up while the front of the discs squeeze together. As a result, pressure on the disc is no longer distributed evenly, and in time one or more of these discs may rupture and squeeze out against a nerve.

Spinal misalignment can also become a serious factor if steps are not taken to correct these existing squatting problems. *Solutions* Reposition the barbell. Instead of carrying it high on your neck, position it low on your neck (powerlifters' style) so that it rests one inch below the top of the posterior deltoid.

The problem of maintaining an upright posture when squatting (this is very evident in bodybuilders who have long thigh bones and a short upper torso) can be overcome in part by squatting with your heels on a two-inch by four-inch board. Above all, make a concentrated effort to maintain an upright posture.

Thighs Becoming Too Large You may find that your thighs are already large enough for your body type and that the squatting movement is starting to make them *too* big. You must keep this body part in harmony with the calf muscle because the bigger your thighs become, the smaller your calves will appear.
Solutions The solution here is to structure the majority of your leg training around exercises like leg extensions, leg curls, supine leg splits, Nautilus inner and outer thigh machine. Stay away from heavy squats of all kinds, preferring high-

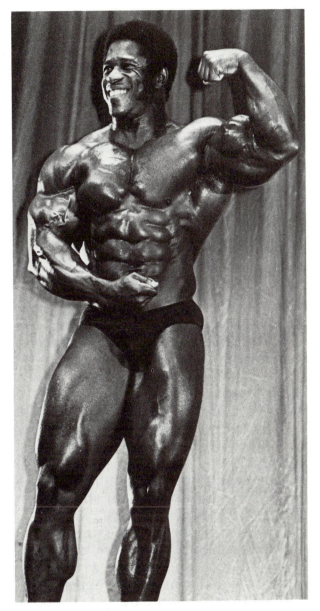

Britain's brawny Bertil Fox.

rep roman chair and sissy squats (body weight only).

Thigh Training

The following thigh programs are those which are the most popular and most effective routines used by today's champions.

Thigh Program I

On this thigh program you will use only the parallel squat. You will perform 10 sets in the following manner: begin your first set with a poundage that will permit you to do 10 solid reps. Add 10 pounds to each succeeding set, decreasing by 1 rep at each set. When you begin your 10th and final set, you will more than likely be able to perform more than 1 rep. Perform as many reps as possible on this final set. Rest only one minute between sets and no more!

Your basic foot position is important to your thigh development. For example, if you point your feet straight forward, you will work the quadriceps; point them out, and the adductors or inner thigh is stressed. Finally, if you point your feet inward (pigeon-toed), you will achieve that outer sweep on the abductors.

Thigh Program II

Simply perform 10 sets of 20 reps in the nonlock barbell squat. This type of program will produce that fibrous, thick, veiny look, but you must use strict form with tension. This will require a poundage you can control without shutting off the tension between the reps.

In other words, keep the weight moving. For example, if you are doing the nonlock barbell squat, slowly, with perfect control, squat down until the upper line of the thigh is just below parallel to the floor. Begin to push yourself up, but just before you reach the knees-locked position, lower yourself back down again.

Remember: Do not rest or pause at any point during the sequence of repetitions during a particular set. This is what keeps the tension on the thigh muscles. The nonlock method of training as we have described it for the barbell squat can be used on many other body parts with

Canada's blonde beauty Deanna Panting— someone to watch in the future.

equal success. This is a favorite training method of "the myth," Sergio Oliva.

Thigh Program III
Front Squats—4 sets, 8 reps
You can do this exercise in the regular fashion or in this unique manner: with a barbell held at the chest clavicular region, under the chin, descend into the lowest squat position possible, pause in this position for a second, then drive hard and fast to rise up to near the standing position (legs should be slightly bent).

Immediately return to the low pause position and repeat the rest of the lift sequence. Remember: Don't bounce at the bottom, but explode when you come out of the bottom position.

Thigh Program IV
Nonlock Squats—6 sets, 8–10 reps
This program consists of regular power squats (5 sets, 8 reps), followed by nonlock squats (1 set, 10 reps). On the nonlock squat, try to add 1 rep at each workout session until you reach 30 reps.

Notes on Squatting

To eliminate stress on the glutes (buttocks) and hips, use a press machine (usually found in commercial gyms or health clubs, sometimes known as a Smith machine) when performing squats. When using this apparatus, your hips are in front of the bar and the torso is leaning backward. If you do not have access to this machine, body-weight sissy squats will do fine. This particular method of squatting gives the illusion of hip slenderness.

Leg Extensions
Rather than sitting in an upright position on this exercise, lie supine or flat on your back on the bench portion, then extend the lower legs until they are perfectly straight or in a locked-out position. Be careful not to overextend on this phase of the movement.

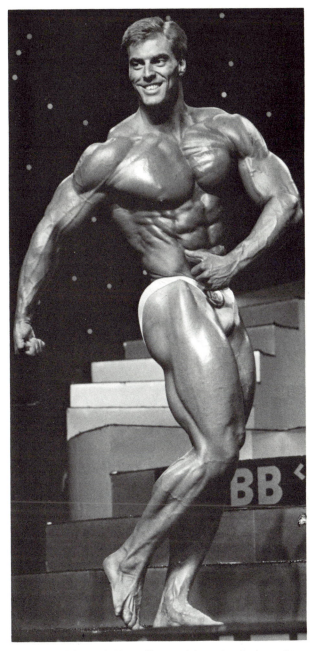

Berry DeMey, Holland's most impressive male bodybuilder.

Pause in the lockout position for five seconds, then slowly return to the starting position. For a slightly different effect on the quads, turn your feet to a pigeon-toed position. This will work the inner quads somewhat.

Of course, if the leg extension machine is of the Nautilus or Dyna Cam or other prototype model that has a back support, you won't be able to do this supine version of the leg extension.

If you are performing leg extensions in the upright position, you should be aware of a couple of things. First, you will find it of some benefit to lean the upper torso back at approximately a 45-degree angle. This angle is instrumental in working the rectus femoris section of the quad muscle.

Your knee angle in the starting position of the leg extension should always approximate a 90-degree angle from the back of the thigh to the front of the shin. If the angle is less than 90 degrees, too much stress is placed on the knee joint at the beginning of the movement.

Jumping Squats

This movement will build tremendous explosiveness for blasting out of the bottom position of the squat. Additionally, it will increase your vertical jumping ability.

The exercise is performed as follows: hold a dumbbell in each hand at the sides; then squat down to below parallel and jump up high (*very* high). When you land, don't stop short; immediately lower into a deep squat position and repeat continuously.

Hack Squats

Here is another great thigh exercise you can do that suggests the nonlock method of training. Don't bottom or top out on this exercise; this way, the thighs are constantly under tension. Hips remain on the bench while going up and off the bench while going down. Keep your heels together, on a block about three inches high and the toes pointed at a 45-degree angle.

CALF SYMMETRY

The biggest enemy of calf improvement is neglect. This neglect stems from the fact that the calf muscle is the least responsive to training when compared to the same training effort applied to such body parts as the biceps and chest.

This lack of responsiveness is due to a number of factors. First, due to everyday activities of walking, running, and just supporting the body weight, the muscles of the calf become very dense and tough. As a result, it is very difficult to break down these muscle fibers and spur them into new growth. Another factor you must take into account is the intramuscular temperature of the calves. The temperature in the calf is about four degrees lower than that of many other muscles in the body. This lower temperature results from less blood circulation due to the pull of gravity, making it very difficult for the blood to circulate and return to the heart. With less circulation, growth in this particular muscle area is slower than it might be in other body parts.

Another factor that contributes to slow growth in this muscle is improper or inadequate contraction of this muscle when exercised. Using poundages in excess of what you are generally capable of on partial-range movements (as opposed to strict full range of motion) is one of the causes of inadequate contraction. The calf is limited in its range of movement (as are the forearms) when compared to that of other muscles in the body. It is therefore very important that you use strict full range of motion in all your calf exercises.

Some authorities in the bodybuilding field suggest that the calf is like any other muscle in the body and can be worked with rep schemes of 8–12 per set. We feel, however, that the calves (and forearms)

The comeback man. After an industrial accident Frank Richards is back—and winning.

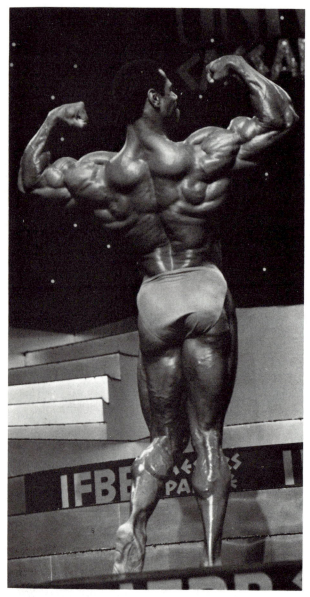

Mike Christian: the world's best back?

limit the size and shape of the calf muscles.

Here is a simple but effective eight-point plan that will help you acquire calf growth and symmetry.

Point Plan

1. The most important apparatus you will be using in your calf program is a block. The height of this block is very important. It should measure at least half the length of your foot. This will allow for the proper stretching methods we will describe later.

2. The shoes you wear during your calf-training session are an important consideration. Use a flexible shoe.

3. Always perform your calf raises on a block. Calf raises done from a flat-footed position, such as on the floor, tend to shorten the ankle tendon, which weakens the arch of the foot. There have even been some isolated cases of back problems with the flat-footed method of calf raises.

4. Place the feet close together (four to six inches apart measured from left to right big toes) when performing the various calf exercises. Placing the feet far apart rather than close tends to make the exercise more difficult because the ankle joint is moving through a shorter range of movement and can't be extended with as much force.

5. Don't do your calf raises with the feet pointed straight ahead during the majority of your sets. During your daily walking, the feet are generally pointed in this direction, and the idea here is to surprise the calf muscle with a new type of stress. Do more of your sets with the toes pointed outward (to work the inner calf) and inward at other times (to work the outer calf).

Do your sets in a two-to-one ratio for the area of the calf needing the most development. For the inner calf, keep your

require more reps than many of the other body parts because, as we have stated, even using full range of motion, the movement is still short at best, and as a result more reps can be performed in the same time frame as other exercises in which 8–12 reps are performed.

It is also agreed that the number of muscle fibers and their attachments will

body weight over the inside of the big toes. For the outer calf, keep the weight of your body on the outer edge of your foot.

6. Due to the poor blood circulation in the calf region we spoke of earlier, it is a good idea to stimulate this body part constantly. There are two methods of providing this stimulation, as follows.

Method No. 1

Because the calf is a relatively small muscle and uses very little in the way of energy substrate, it can be worked very hard every day for up to three months. At the conclusion of this time period, it would be a good idea to give the calves two weeks to let them soften up a bit before pursuing another three-month period of vigorous work.

While the calves can and probably should be exercised every day in some cases to stimulate blood circulation, it isn't a good idea to work this muscle extremely hard every day. The calf, like other muscle groups, must have periods of rest to spur growth.

With this thought in mind, you might approach your calf training in this proven

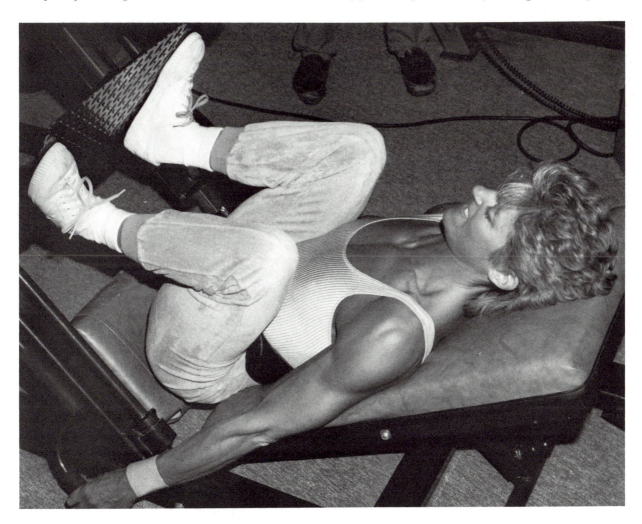

45-degree leg press by Carolyn Cheshire.

manner: work the calves extremely hard every other day. This means using heavy poundages while maintaining strict form and a variety of exercises.

On alternate days, just pump this muscle to increase the circulation capacity. Do this by performing three sets of body-weight-only two-leg and/or one-leg calf raises. Do your reps to absolute failure on these sets.

On these pump days, always make a conscious effort to contract the calves to their absolute limit and stretch them to their limit. The stretching is as important in developing the calves as are the contractions.

Here is how the heel raise and stretching movements should be performed for best overall results:

Begin your set by keeping the knees in a slightly unlocked position. Now slowly and with deliberation (no cheating) rise as high on the toes as possible on each repetition. Mentally try to rise even higher. Look straight up at the ceiling, which will really help.

Now lower to the bottom position and stretch even lower if possible. If there is a secret to calf development, it is the stretch at the bottom of the movement. After you have completed your calf routine, finish off with some body-weight-only calf stretching. This should be done for at least 15 minutes to 30 minutes on each foot, depending on your time allowance.

This movement should always be done on your calf block so that you will benefit from a complete stretch.

Begin by putting all your body weight on one leg. Keep the knees locked and the hips forward. Curl the toes up. Now, while standing on one leg, very quickly bounce up and down to stretch the calf. Stretch at the bottom position until you cannot stand the pain. Then shift to the other leg.

Boyer Coe uses special leg shoes to build his calves.

Alternate back and forth for the required time limits.

Go easy on stretching because it can result in very painful and sore calves your first time out. This method of training the calf is a favorite of multi–Mr. Universe winner and Olympia contender Boyer Coe.

After you have finished stretching your calves, place your calf block directly under your heels and rapidly raise and lower the toes (50 fast contractions) while keeping the heels on the board. This particular exercise will cause a cramping effect in the shin area. At first it will be enough to do this exercise without any added resistance. But later you will have to use a method whereby you place added resistance on the toe area. This particular movement will add to the appearance of the calf, especially when it is viewed from the front.

Method No. 2
Don't rest more than 30–45 seconds between sets. These short rest periods will allow you to maintain a maximum pump within the calf. To further the effects of maximum circulation in the calf, many top bodybuilders have found applying an analgesic balm to the calf muscle between sets to be helpful.

On the days that you work the thighs, structure your calf program immediately after your last exercise and set of thigh work. The heavy squats, leg presses, and leg extensions have demanded that literally huge amounts of blood be sent to this lower extremity, and this is much needed for proper calf stimulation.

7. Experiment with different calf rou-

Rich Gaspari and his former training partner Lee Haney.

Kevin Lawrence and Diana Dennis, two of the most dynamic physiques on the pairs circuit today.

Juliette Bergman trains her lats.

LATS

For optimum growth and shape in this muscle, reps of 8–12 seem to work best. You also must always keep the lats under continuous tension. Don't lock out the arms on your lat exercises, and you will be sure to achieve this tension factor.

Reviewing the Exercise Selection Chart in Chapter 5, you should take note of a few of the listed lat exercises. Lat pulldowns and wide-grip pullups to the back of the neck, for example, will add greater width to the lat, while heavy bent-over rowing will create the desired lat density or thickness.

On these bent-over rows, it is a good idea to wear a lifting belt. This will alleviate any abdominal pressures that might otherwise occur.

Concentrate on isolating and spreading the lats as much as possible on each rep as you return to the starting position on an exercise. Earlier, we mentioned the value of performing burns at the top contracted position of an exercise. These can also be done at the starting position. Try this method in the lat pulldown at the top position (which is the starting position of this exercise), and you will find it great for separation of the muscles of the back.

The contracted position of the various lat exercises is equally important to overall progress. On the final rep of a particular set, it is a good idea to hold the contracted position for a six-second count. This practice is very beneficial for recruiting neuromuscular nerve facilitation in the muscle.

To shock the lats, try using the triangular approach. The idea here is to begin your lat program by using an overhead exercise such as the lat pulldown. This will pull the lats up and outward. After you have completed this exercise for the

tines and apparatus until you find a program that works best for you.

A closing note on calf symmetry: if you are interested in building astounding calves, you will want to add the Legg Shoe to your training program. These shoes create such an overload in the calf and surrounding muscles that if you did nothing more than walk around in them you would still achieve fantastic leg development.

If you are interested in more information on this training item, write to Boyer Coe at PO Box 1321, Rancho Mirage, CA 92270-1321.

required sets and reps, move on to an exercise from the floor such as heavy bent-over rowing. This exercise will work the thickness in the upper back. Now finish off the program with a horizontal pulley movement such as seated cable rowing. This will add thickness and width from a different angle.

Between sets of these lat exercises, you might find it valuable to perform 10–20 seconds of lat stretching.

Lat Stretches

To your pullup or chinup bar, attach two pieces of webbing with heavy stitched loops in each end. These loops can be made from Scuba weight belt material.

Now stand on a stool and loop your wrists through the webbing. From this position, step off the stool and lower yourself to arm's length into a dead-hang position from the pullup bar. Competely stretch your lats from this position. Work up to one or two minutes in this position per set.

Use additional poundage around your waist for maximum intensity. This is a favorite lat stretching exercise of former Mr. World Chuck Sipes.

SPINAE ERECTORS

One of the very best exercises for this muscle is the Prone hyperextension, but done with this variation: when you are in the back arch position (parallel to the floor), hold this for about 30 seconds while you twist your upper torso or trunk from right to left to right, etc.

Don't bend at the waist from side to side, but twist the trunk. This will be hard to do at first, but is well worth the effort! Practice with your own body weight at first, then add poundage by holding a barbell plate to the chest or behind the neck, as in situps.

This is a very good optional exercise for those of you who do not wish to perform the deadlift exercise or its variations.

Chest

Most bodybuilders rely too much on the supine bench press for chest development when in fact it is better to do more incline barbell and dumbbell work, which works the upper chest area.

The degree of incline that works this segment of the chest is approximately 35 degrees. Inclines beyond this figure tend to stress the frontal or posterior deltoid, and that is not the muscle you are attempting to stimulate with this exercise.

Also, if you should decide to use dumbbells as a means of working the upper chest (and this is a very good exercise for obtaining a deeper, fuller stretch within the upper pecs), be sure that all four parts of the dumbbell face each other (palms facing each other) when pressing, which will prevent the delt from kicking in as well.

This advice can be applied to flat supine and decline dumbbell presses as well.

Flat Flyes

On the flat flyes with dumbbells, isolate the movement further by keeping your feet off the floor. This can be accomplished by doing a modified position of the knee pullin while performing the flyes.

Prevent injury to the elbows by keeping the arms bent just slightly. You also might want to use an ace bandage or a neoprene elbow pad to add support to the elbow region.

To get the maximum amount of stimulation from this movement, work at throwing the dumbbells (in a very controlled manner) out from the body as far as possible. Now, as you bring the bells together at the top contracted position (basically, this movement will be like hugging a tree), flex the wrist back and mentally contract the pecs.

Straight-Arm Pullovers

For complete chest development, always include some variation of the pullover to work the rib cage. The poundage is not as important here as is really working for a deep stretch within the rib cage.

The use of heavy poundages in the straight-arm pullover tends to contract the latissimus muscle, and this in turn contracts against the rib cage. Likewise, the abdominal muscles will contract against the rib cage if the feet are allowed to remain on the floor. To counteract this, simply follow the advice for isolation of the feet given for the flat flyes.

Another thing you can do to isolate the various muscles that might interfere with rib cage expansion is to relax the

Scott Wilson trains his lats.

Chuck Williams and Charles Glass.

tricep muscles as much as possible when you begin to lower the bar over your head.

The most advanced bodybuilder shouldn't have to use more than 50 pounds in this particular exercise, and beginners and intermediates much less. Deep breathing and maximum rib cage expansion are the requirement, not poundage lifted!

Here is a unique mini-chest routine you might want to do at the conclusion of your chest workout: for a period of three months and twice per week, do your bench presses with 100 pounds and for no more than two sets; do as many reps as possible. Always try to do more each workout! Don't settle for less than one additional rep per workout. Rest two to three minutes between these sets.

After these sets are completed, do one or two sets of freehand body-weight-only pushups in the same manner. Do your pushups over an empty exercise bar that is positioned securely on the floor. Grasp this bar with your regular bench press grip. You will experience a tremendous pump from this mini-routine.

DELTOIDS

Here are a few of our favorite deltoid exercises.

Dumbbell Side Laterals

To ensure that you are working the lateral or side deltoid, point the front of the bells slightly downward as you reach the crucifix position of the movement. This will isolate the lateral delt without letting the anterior or front delt kick in. It is important that you follow this instruction because this exercise is instrumental in giving the illusion of greater shoulder width.

Since lateral raises are a leverage-type

exercise, they do not allow you to handle much weight (as opposed to shoulder pressing movements), but they have proven to be the best type of exercise for isolation of a specific muscle segment such as the lateral deltoid.

On all lateral movements, the arms should be slightly unlocked to relieve excess pressure and strain on the elbow insertions.

Upright Rowing with a Barbell

On this exercise, pick a spot on the ceiling and look up at it. Thus you will be able to obtain a higher pull, though you will not want to pull higher than eye level because the traps tend to kick in after this point.

Keep this barbell four inches in front of the body at all times.

Seated Presses

The bench you use when doing seated presses should be at a height that will permit your legs to bend at a 90-degree angle. This will help you prevent cramping in the hip region, which occurs when the legs are at smaller angles than advised.

Supine Front Arm Raise

Lie supine on an exercise bench and hold a barbell overhead, using your normal bench press grip. Now lower the barbell down to the upper thighs (arms always remain straight) until it just barely touches the body.

Raise the barbell back up to the overhead position and repeat for the number of reps you plan to do. This movement is terrific for very necessary deltoid power in the various bench press exercises.

Wide-Grip Collar-to-Collar Bent-over Rowing

There are many good rear deltoid exercises, but one that such champions as Boyer Coe have found to work this area most effectively is the wide-grip collar-to-collar bent-over rowing movement.

This exercise has always been thought to be a lat developer. However, it works best for the rear deltoid, but it must be done in extremely strict style, slowly and smoothly.

BICEPS

Here are a few of the most effective bicep exercises.

Seated Barbell Curls

Sit on an exercise bench with a barbell resting on your thighs, upper arms and elbows at your side (never move elbows from this position), palms up; now curl the barbell up toward the chest. The bar cannot be brought to touch the chest, obviously, if the elbows don't move. As a result, there will be a great cramping of the biceps at the high contracted position of the curl. Lower the barbell to the thighs (just barely touching).

The Scott Barbell Curl

These curls are superior for developing the low bicep connection. The angle of the Scott or preacher bench should be anywhere from a minimum of 45 degrees to as much as 90 degrees.

Body positon and hand spacing are important to the success of these curls. The top of the padded bench should be two to four inches below the sternal (or lower) pectoralis muscle. This position will allow you to develop a nice round bicep, as opposed to sinking the top of the Scott bench directly under the armpits near the upper pecs, developing a flat bicep.

The hand spacing you take on this exercise determines to some degree which segment of the bicep you will be working. For instance, an 11-inch spacing between the little fingers of the hands (elbows same width) will develop the belly of the bicep. A 3-inch to 4-inch hand spacing between the little fingers (elbows 16–18 inches apart) or an ultrawide grip of 24 inches (elbows will be approximately 15 inches apart) will work the inner bicep.

Scott Dumbbell Curls

Be sure that you maintain a constant tension on the muscle, especially at the bottom position. If you relax at the bottom of the movement, it will be very easy to hyperextend the elbows, thus causing trauma and injury. It is also a good idea to wear some type of supportive elbow pads when doing the Scott curls.

TRICEPS

Lying French Press

On this valuable exercise, be sure to use an EZ Curl bar rather than a straight bar. The EZ Curl bar will help to eliminate elbow and tricep injury due to its more favorable mechanical leverages.

Lying supine on an exercise bench, take a grip in which your hands are spaced three to five inches apart. The elbows remain high and pointed toward the ceiling.

Be sure not to move the elbows, and slowly lower the barbell to the nose or forehead. Do not bounce the barbell at this low position. Extend and lock out the triceps.

A regular exercise bench is fine as long as you have some way to rack the weight upon completion of a set. If you don't, we suggest you use a bench that is only six or so inches off the floor. This low bench will allow you to lift the barbell off the floor without hurting yourself.

Here is a training procedure you might want to try for the triceps. Perform 1 set of 12 reps of the strict triceps pressdown on the lat machine, using a medium amount of poundage. Next add more poundage to the lat machine and perform 3–4 sets of the one-half triceps pressdown, using the lower (lockout) half of the movement.

Use a movement of about six inches or so and a heavy poundage. After the one-half pressdowns, decrease the poundage and perform 1 set of 12 reps.

FOREARM POWER

Forearm power is very much a matter of intense mental concentration. It is easy to work for maximum power and forearm size more frequently than on some other larger body parts like the thighs since less energy is used and the recovery time between workouts is minimal.

If it is your ambition to develop great gripping power, we suggest you try some of these proven exercises.

One-Hand Deadlifts

This exercise is performed in a straddle lift style, where the bar is between your legs on the floor. Reach down and grasp the bar while handling as much poundage as possible for the number of reps you plan to do.

It might be a good idea to use a hook

Corinna Everson during her winning Ms. Olympia routine.

Bill Grant and Samir Bannout.

grip since this keeps the hand from slipping as much as it would with a standard grip. By the hook grip, we mean taking a good grip with the fingers (index and middle) wrapped around the end of the thumbs.

At first, this exercise may discourage you because the grip seems to be the limiting factor, but as you continue to train on this type of lift you will find your grip getting stronger and stronger.

Rectangular Fix or Reverse Curl

Old-time strongman George F. Jowett improved his grip momentarily by performing this exercise as part of his forearm power program. It is done as follows:

1. Warm up by performing 2 sets of 8–10 reps of light-heavy reverse curls in regular style. Rest one minute.

2. Take a barbell at the top position of the reverse curl exercise and lower the barbell until the forearms are parallel to the floor. Hold this position for three to five seconds; then, without any body momentum, reverse-curl the barbell back up to the top position (this is your starting position, rather than the regular position where the barbell is hanging at arm's length, touching the thighs). This is one rep. Try doing three to four sets of five reps in the manner described.

Eliminate elbow movement by strapping your arms to your sides with a belt (a training partner can do this for you).

This exercise was one of many that Jowett used to improve his grip to the point that he was able to grip a 170-pound blacksmith anvil by the horn with one hand and clean and press it overhead!

Sliding Pinch Grip

Take two metal Olympic plates (begin light and work up to using two 45-pound-ers) and place them together so that the smooth surfaces are on the outside. Now, without the aid of chalk on your hands, proceed to pinch-grip the plates and walk a definite distance until your grip fails. Perform this exercise from one to three times with each hand.

Measure your progress in this sliding pinch grip exercise by determining the distance you walk and by poundage increases. This was a favorite of John C. Grimek.

If, for some reason, you don't have access to Olympic plates, you can load up two heavy dumbbells, then lubricate the palms of your hands generously with petroleum jelly and walk around with the dumbbells until you just can't hold them any longer. Do this for at least three maximum attempts.

Sustaining Power Gripping

Use a heavy-duty hand gripper. Squeeze the handles together and hold for two minutes. Place a piece of leather between the closed handles to provide full closure; leather will fall out if grip weakens.

You can even tie a small weight (three to five ounces) to this leather and hang from a 12-inch length of twine. Alternate hands. As your strength increases, add more time to this effort; never do it for less time than you did in the preceding workout!

If you are interested in an exercise that will primarily develop size in the belly of the forearm, you will appreciate the accompanying illustration and instruction for the dumbbell wrist curl with the upper arm parallel.

This is another favorite of Chuck Sipes. He was known for his massive and vascular forearms, which measured over 18 inches during his prime.

Dumbbell Wrist Curl
with Upper Arm Parallel

As usual, the forearm is laid along the top of the thigh, with the hand and the lower part of the wrist extending off the end of the knee.

The unusual thing about this movement involves the upper torso. The torso is twisted slightly to bring the shoulder of the working side closer to the wrist.

Continue leaning forward and to the outside until the upper arm of the curling hand is parallel to the floor, or as near parallel as you can make it. Remain in this position while you perform the dumbbell wrist curl. Concentrate strongly on the movement.

If there is a secret to this exercise or any other wrist-curling movement, it is always keeping your hips higher than your knees and your elbows higher than your wrist. The upper torso should lean forward until the angle between the biceps and forearms is less than 90 degrees. This posture or body position will effectively isolate the flexor muscles in the forearms when the wrist curl is done in a palms-up position, as in the above exercise. Perform the exercise with the palms down, and you will isolate the extensor muscles.

As a final note on forearm power, you can develop greater gripping strength by increasing the diameter of your barbell and dumbbell bars. This can be done by purchasing a material called Armoflex (be sure to ask for the 1⅛- or 1¼-inch-inside-diameter size) from your local plumbing and heating store.

Generally, you will want to cut two pieces of this material slightly longer than the width of your hand. Increasing the diameter of your exercise bars with this Armoflex will cause you to grip the bar extra-tight, and this in turn will help build a tenacious grip.

Another way the Armoflex can be used (you will have some extra left over because most generally it is sold in six-foot lengths) is on your squat bar. This will add some comfort to the bar as it sits on your shoulders for a set of 20-rep squats.

All in all, even when you have developed what you might consider a powerful grip, it is the grip that gives out or is the limiting factor in such exercises as chin-ups, cable rows, lat pulldowns, and shrugs, as well as many other exercises.

If you are interested in doing a few more reps in some of these mentioned exercises, you will certainly be interested in purchasing a pair of power grips. These are far superior to conventional training gloves and straps. Write to Power Grip, P.O. Box 1, Catasauqua, PA 18032.

Above all, remember that the grip is represented in many barbell and dumbbell exercises so that it is best to round out your workout program with forearm-building and grip exercises as the last group of exercises in your daily workout.

ABDOMINAL TRAINING

The abdominals are usually one of the last muscle groups to be given quality training time. Yet no other body part can give the physique that finished and mature look like a ripped, cut-up, midsection.

Anyone can have a tight trim waist by following the proper techniques for abdominal training.

The basic function of the abdominals is to pull the rib cage and pelvis together. Properly toned abdominals assist in keeping the pelvis at the proper angle (up and back), and this in turn keeps the spinal column straight.

Facts on the Abs

1. Most exercises classified as abdominal exercises do not contribute to the majority of abdominal stimulation, but in fact work the hip flexor muscles, which are located in the middle of the thigh region, run through the pelvic region, and attach to the spinal region of the lower back.

2. An exercise will qualify as an abdominal exercise only if the feet are not anchored or secured to the floor (as would be the case in such exercises as regular and/or incline situps, roman chair situps, and even the various forms of the hanging leg raise, because the gravitational pull on the legs causes the hip flexors to receive the majority of the work) and you do not perform the movement beyond 30 degrees of the actual movement from the starting position. Again, any movement beyond the specified 30 degrees of the actual movement will increase hip flexor activity. This can be a very serious problem for those of you who have back problems.

3. For those of you who experience this type of problem, we suggest that you structure your frontal abdominal program around the frog situps or crunches and its variations and the lying six-inch leg raise. The crunch is one of the purest frontal abdominal exercises in existence, and we feel that it deserves a detailed explanation.

Crunches

Lie on your back on the floor. You can position your lower torso in one of two ways: either rest your calves on a bench in the gym or on a bed at home in such a way that your thighs are more or less vertical or simply cross your legs Indian-style while lying on the floor. Either of these two methods will keep the hip flexors from participating in the actual movement.

Place your hands (interlocked) behind your head and expel all the air out of your chest cavity. This is very important because it will help create tension in the abdominals. Now begin to sit up. When you are doing this (and remember that your back must never go beyond 30 degrees off the floor, which will be only a few inches at most), mentally try to curl your pelvis and lower ribs until they touch for maximal contraction of the frontal abdominals.

You won't actually be able to do this physically, but the mental focus will certainly help you acquire a tight crunch.

Hold this position for two seconds and repeat. It is important for you to realize that your hands behind your head should be relaxed at all times through the movement and should not assist in any way (which might include pulling against the neck).

4. The abdominals are slow-twitch muscles, which means that they have quite a capacity for endurance-type train-

ing, so high reps are the order of the day. You generally will want to do 15–25 reps per set, though this does vary somewhat from the abdominal programs listed in the chapter on bodybuilding specialization.

5. Many bodybuilders feel that because the abdominal muscles are slow-twitch muscles the repetition must be done slowly on each exercise affecting this body part. The speed of the repetition of an abdominal exercise is *not* related to the fast-/slow-twitch theory.

We recommend that the abdominal exercises be done slowly for behavioral reasons. It turns out that most bodybuilders tend to do many of the abdominal exercises, especially the crunch, ballistically if we tell them to do them at a medium cadence. Experimentation has revealed that the greater percentage of bodybuilders who do abdominal exercises correctly—and realize maximum benefits from them—have been instructed to do the movement slowly beforehand. Of course, there is the other school of thought, which suggests that you use the speed you like to use, whether it is digging a ditch or painting a house. There is a speed each person enjoys moving at, and then it is just a matter of doing the movement deliberately while minimizing rest time more than the speed of the repetitions.

6. The best abdominal reducer is a proper diet; if you don't follow a proper low-fat diet all your exercises will be for naught.

General Comments

Those of you who do not have any lower back problems, and for the pure delight of it enjoy the various abdominal exercises in which the hip flexors are stressed, might benefit from the following comments.

For developing density, thickness, and hardness in the abs, perform more sets and fewer reps (5–10 sets/8–10 reps) on the high incline (30–45 degrees) situp board, with the knees bent and a weight held behind the head.

Be very careful that you do not go overboard on this exercise because too much size will cause the abdominals to protrude farther than the chest.

From time to time, it is a good idea to vary the angle of the adjustable incline situp board to apply maximum stress to the various sections of the abdominals. This training concept can be carried to the point where you might begin at the top rung of the adjustable ladder and perform as many bent-knee situps as possible and then immediately turn over on your back and perform the decline leg raise movement. Without a pause, position the board on the next rung down and repeat the entire process as we have described it until you are down to the bottom of the ladder.

This procedure works very well going from the bottom to the top, too. Regardless of the procedure you follow, it is very important that you use extreme control and tension throughout each rep of each abdominal exercise. Cheating or sloppy form will not build thick, hard abdominals.

On an abdominal apparatus such as the roman chair, you can intensify the movement by putting a six-inch block of wood under the front of the unit.

Your back should never break parallel to the floor on the roman chair movement; too much stress is placed on the lower back. Speaking of stress on the lower back from certain abdominal exercises, you can immediately see the rationale in not doing abdominal work prior to a heavy squatting or deadlift session. Along with this, the back is used in many pressing move-

Ed Kawak shows his turtle shell abs!

Rich Gaspari between poses.

Many bodybuilders have found that for abdominal training, at least, five daily training sessions consisting of 5 minutes each are better for progress than one continuous 25-minute session. For example, in one session you might use the adjustable incline situp board technique we spoke about earlier. At another session, you might use isotension, where you flex the abdominals very hard in front of a mirror. This was one of Frank Zane's Mr. Olympia training secrets. Finally, another session could consist of performing stomach suctions. This exercise adapts itself quite well to those times in the day when you might be walking, driving, reading, and in some cases working.

For those of you who are not familiar with this exercise, this brief explanation should suffice: exhale all the air out of your lungs. Now instead of inhaling, pull your stomach as high into your rib cage area, while your stomach is empty, as possible. Hold this position as long as you can. Relax the stomach and take another breath and again expel the air from the lungs and begin the sequence over again. Mentally vacuum your stomach harder with each attempt to achieve that deep aching sensation.

The Abs—Bits of Advice

1. Always perform your abdominal exercises on an empty stomach.
2. When structuring an ab program, be sure to work the lowers first in the program, then the obliques, and finish off the program by working the upper abs. Larry Scott, a two-time Mr. Olympia winner, says that if you work the lower abs hard the uppers will take care of themselves, though this does not mean you are not to work the upper abs. In reality, it is hard to work the

ments overhead and is the support muscle in exercises like the standing two-arm barbell curl.

Taking all of this into consideration, it is better to structure your abdominal training as near the end of a daily workout schedule as possible.

lower abs without strongly involving the upper area.

3. Proper posture is vitally important to abdominal tone. Therefore, upon arising in the morning (just before you get dressed), tie a string around your waist. You should be in a correct upright posture when you do this. The string should not be so tight as to cut into your circulation, but tight enough that if your posture fails during the day or you are overeating (stomach is beginning to swell or bloat) it will cut into your waist just enough to remind you either to stand straight or to slow down on your eating habit.

THE NECK

Neck work will increase the blood supply to the brain and also aid in the reduction of a double chin. The neck is composed of soft muscle tissue. The immediate advantage of this soft muscle tissue is the fact that it is very responsive to training and not much work is needed to increase its size and strength.

One to two months of specialization will usually bring out the maximum in size and strength. This statement is not in contradiction to what was mentioned in the previous paragraph. One to two months is minimal when compared to the time involved in specialization procedures for some other body parts. After a properly initiated program of this nature, the gains can be maintained with as few as one to two workouts per week.

One of the most effective ways to build up the back of the neck is by doing the neck bridge. This is done in the following manner:

Lie on your back with your head on the floor. You may use a pillow for comfort.

Now, by the strength of the neck muscles alone, begin to bridge or raise your body off the floor. Your back will be completely off the floor and arched, your feet directly under the knees.

If you have not been doing neck exercises on a regular basis, the most you will want to do here is hold this position without any further movement. Your goal over the next few weeks is to work up to holding the bridge posture for three or four minutes.

When you can accomplish this feat, you are ready for some neck bridge movements, which consist of getting into the position described and rocking back and forth from the crown of your head and as far toward the forehead as possible. Lower yourself back down to the floor until your back is touching again. This is one rep. Work up to 25 reps for a couple of sets in this exercise. When you accomplish this goal, it is time to begin (slowly) using progressive weight resistance in which you hold a barbell plate or light barbell over your chest while performing the neck bridge.

Some of the old-time strongmen used to position themselves in the neck bridge position and perform a modified barbell bench press.

One of the best ways to work the front of the neck is to lie supine on an exercise bench, with your head extended over the end of it. Now place a folded towel on your forehead for padding and place a barbell plate on your forehead. Hold the plate in place with your hands and, through neck action alone, lower or extend your head as far back as possible. This is called the *posterior extension* of the movement and works the back of the neck.

Now smoothly raise or move your head toward the chest to achieve anterior flexion and thereby work the front of the neck.

After the initial workout for the neck that we mentioned earlier, follow the Holistic Training Guide in Chapter 2 for a specific exercise and the rep and set application.

The use of a neck strap is a very valuable training aid. It can be used to develop the neck muscles in a manner similar to that described for the above exercises.

Also, by lying on your side on a flat exercise bench with your head hanging off the end, you can adjust the neck strap in such a way as to work the laterals or sides of the neck.

Many bodybuilders tend to forgo the above-mentioned progressive weight resistance neck exercises in favor of human-resistance-only movements with a training partner. The most common fault we find with this approach to neck training or similar dynamic tension methods is this: you may have the capacity to endure 100 pounds of neck resistance for a one-rep maximum in the posterior extension of the movement. Your training partner may apply 80 pounds of resistance (which is appropriate for an 8- to 12-rep count) to the neck for each and every rep of the set. If you are fortunate, your training partner may apply the proper resistance for all the required sets of the back-of-the-neck exercise. Now, during the next scheduled workout for the neck, your training partner begins applying the proper resistance to the neck, but for some unknown reason, right in the middle of a good set, he is applying only 24 pounds of resistance for the remaining few reps of the set.

A muscle will only begin an adaptive response very slightly to exercise at a minimal 35 percent of your one-rep maximum. In this case, that would be 35 pounds, and the 24 pounds of resistance

Anita Gandol shows her beautiful physique.

from the training partner would not be meeting this demand.

Now, the next set is dramatically different from the one we just mentioned. Your training partner's mind is just not into the workout, and during this set he begins to apply 125 pounds of resistance. This quite naturally exceeds your strength capabilities in the back-of-the-neck movement (posterior extension).

An injury occurs because, as you might remember, your limit was 100 pounds for a single maximum attempt, and the 125 pounds exceeded that by 25 percent.

This situation is only hypothetical in nature, but as you can see, there is just no method by which to accurately measure the resistance applied by a training partner to exercises like this. Even the various dynamic tension methods in which you apply resistance to yourself have the same type of problem.

A good example of this is a shoulder exercise in which your left arm is hanging free and slightly to the rear. You grip the crook of the elbow of this arm from the back by the right hand. Now endeavor to pull the left arm forward while resisting strongly with the right hand. How do you gauge the amount of resistance you are applying to this exercise? You can't! One rep you might resist with 50 pounds of force, and the next rep it might be 65 pounds.

Progressive resistance weight training, body-weight-only exercises, or any other method in which you can measure resistance or force applied is the better approach to training.

Rich Gaspari—muscle on top of muscle.

9
THE CHAMPIONS' SECRET—AEROBICS

After many years of research and physiological studies, exercise scientists have shown that aerobics are a most efficient means by which to improve the heart, lungs, and circulatory system and to burn up body fat. In fact, an aerobic training session will continue to burn fat calories for as long as 12–14 hours later, which makes aerobics one of competitive bodybuilding's secrets to getting ripped and cut up.

Aerobic training is any mild (low-stress) exercise that is performed nonstop for at least 12 minutes and up to as much as 1 hour per session and on at least three alternate days per week and in some cases five or six times per week.

This style of exercise must also sustain your pulse rate at an active 60 percent and no more than 80 percent of an age-adjusted maximum heart rate continuously for the time (minutes) indicated. What constitutes quality aerobic training? Your heart rate, resting and active, is the most important consideration. There are four factors that determine your heart rate:

1. Maximum heart rate—Two hundred twenty beats per minute is the maximum you can sustain under the most active conditions, and this maximum changes according to . . .

2. Age—At birth the heart is capable of the demands mentioned above. As an internal safety mechanism, the maximum heart rate will decrease by one stroke for each additional year of life. For example, at the age of 20, your heart rate usually will not exceed 200 beats per minute at its highest intensity.

3. Resting Pulse Rate—This is the number of times your heart beats at rest (nonexercise state). The normal resting pulse for a healthy male is 63–72 beats per minute and 69–80 beats per minute for a female.

For the extremely fit male and female athletes, the resting pulse will in some cases be under 52 beats per minute and 58 beats per minute respectively. On the other end of the aerobic fitness scale, a resting pulse that exceeds 88 for a male and 94 for a female should be considered extremely poor. Those of you who are in this category should have a stress EKG test. This test will accurately determine the present condition of your heart.

For those of you who wish to examine your resting pulse rate, the most accurate means is of course a pulse-monitoring device. There are also, however, a couple of self tests you can perform (see sidebar).

4. Aerobic Training Heart Rate—This is the most efficient rate at which your heart should beat during a quality aerobic training session. Why? Because if the heart beats beyond the computed aerobic formula, your body will burn more glucose than fat.

This aerobic training efficiency strengthens the oxygen-processing mechanism, which in turn is able to withstand lactic acid buildup (this is the metabolic waste that causes the termination of a muscle contraction).

HOW TO ACHIEVE PROPER TRAINING HEART RATE

To achieve the proper training heart rate, adhere to the following guidelines.

1. Begin your aerobic sessions at a

Training Heart Rate Formula

A couple of methods will determine the training heart rate that is right for you. The first way is to deduct your age in years from 220. You then take that answer and multiply it by the percentage you select, whether it be the base requirement of 60 percent or any percentage up to the 80 percent maximum.

For example, if you are 38 years old, and you decide to use a 60-percent minimum, your training heart rate would be approximately 109.
$$220 - 38 = 182. \quad 182 \times .60 = 109.$$

The problem with this formula is that the heart rate is based on a resting pulse of 72 for the male and 80 for a female. What if your resting pulse is 70 or below in the above example for the male? This formula would not be totally accurate.

The word accuracy brings up a point

regarding the difference in the formula applications for men and women. Women should add 10 to their age and then deduct that figure from 220 and then carry out the remaining mathematical steps necessary to compute the training heart rate.

The second method is the Karounen computation, which calls for deducting your age and resting pulse from 220.
$$220 - 38 - 70 = 112$$

Now take the subtotal of 112 and multiply it by the percentage of the age-adjusted heart rate you have selected. In this case, let's use 60 percent.
$$112 \times .60 = 67$$

Now take 67 and add it to your resting pulse of 70.
$$67 + 70 = 137$$

As you can see, there is some difference between the two methods as to determining your training heart rate. You and you alone must decide which method is best for you.

Vera Bendel pumps up backstage.

minimum of 60 percent of your age-adjusted maximum heart rate and gradually, over a period of weeks, work up to 80 percent of the age-adjusted heart rate—and absolutely no more! There are two very good reasons for this:

- An age-adjusted heart rate of less than 60 percent will not be enough to cause

the necessary adaptive responses in aerobic efficiency. In many cases even heart attack victims will train aerobically at slightly more than 60 percent at their very first session.

- Exercise that is strenuous in nature and performed at more than 80 percent of an age-adjusted maximum puts you into an anaerobic state (which depends upon glucose/glycogen as energy substrate). In addition, this hard work would require prolonged periods of rest between exercises, which lowers the pulse rate and level of breathing well below the aerobic requirements.

2. An aerobic session should last a minimum of 12 continuous minutes at the proper age-adjusted heart rate. This is a good time to begin monitoring your pulse, because some exercises may take as long as 5–10 minutes before you reach the proper heart rate. For example, if it takes you 10 minutes to reach your correct active heart rate on jumping jacks, then you would be looking at a time factor of 22 minutes of aerobic activity. This is only an illustration, and in most cases it shouldn't take you more than 3–5 minutes to reach your target time on any exercise you might choose.

You can train in an aerobic fashion for as much as 60 minutes per session, although usually after an hour or more muscle tissue as well as fat is burned, and you certainly don't need that. On the average, 25–30 minutes of quality aerobic training offers some of the best results.

3. You should train a minimum of three alternate days per week and may even extend this to a maximum of five to six days.

4. If you have a problem gaining muscular body weight but desire to train aerobically, simply follow points 2 and 3 above at the minimum levels.

Those of you who are overweight

Measuring Your Resting Pulse Rate

Use one of the two following methods.

1. Place your index finger on the carotid artery on the neck. This is a main artery located alongside the Adam's apple on the right side of the neck. Sometimes it is difficult to locate this major pulse area, so you might try tilting your head back and laterally to the left.

2. Another self-test involves lightly touching the vein that runs along the surface of the wrist, palm side up, and is in line with the thumb.

PULSE ACCURACY

The most accurate method of taking a pulse reading, whether it be a resting or an active training pulse, is to count the number of heart beats (be sure to count quarter and half beats) for six seconds and then multiply that figure by 10 to compute your pulse rate for one minute.

For extreme accuracy in determining your average resting pulse, take random readings three to four times per day (upon arising, at noontime, in the evening, etc.) for approximately seven days in a row to begin with.

This advice can be applied to your aerobic training sessions as well. After a period of time it won't be necessary to monitor your resting and active (aerobic) rates as frequently as initially advised. Once or twice a week should do it. Be sure that any and all pulse readings are taken while you are in a healthy state.

Don't . . .

- Take a pulse with your thumb as it has its own pulse beat and will give a false reading.
- Take a pulse reading under stressful situations (this does not include athletic events and training modes) as stress can cause rapid increases in the pulse rate.
- Take a pulse reading when you have the flu or fever or while using medications.

A TRAINING TIP

For those of you who are into heavy athletic training and wish to know if you are approaching a state of overtraining, monitor your pulse three mornings in succession. If your resting pulse is 10 or more beats higher than normal, it is possible you are overtraining and need to decrease your training quotas somewhat.

should gradually, over the next few weeks, work up to the maximums suggested in points 2 and 3 above.

All of you, regardless of your physical condition or goals, should follow point 1 exactly as stated.

THE TWO-MINUTE HEALTH INDICATOR

Exercise scientists universally agree that monitoring the heart rate immediately following a workout will give you a pretty good idea of the overall fitness of your heart. This is accomplished by taking a pulse immediately following an exercise, then exactly one minute later taking your pulse once again. Subtract the second reading from the first and divide by 10.

For example, let's suppose that your exercise heart rate is 137, you wait one minute exactly and take your pulse again, and this time it has decreased to 85. Subtract 85 from 137 = 52. Divide 52 by 10 and you will come up with a figure of 5. The following list will clarify the meaning of this number.

Less than 2...Poor
2–3...........Fair
3–4..........Good
4–6......Excellent
6 or more...Super

The heart rate indicator shows that your computed figure of 5 puts your heart fitness in the excellent category. If for some reason your heart rate recovers faster than in 1 minute, simply take your pulse reading immediately after you exercise and then 30 seconds later, rather than after 60 seconds. Go through the subtraction procedure and then divide by 5 rather than 10. This variation will most

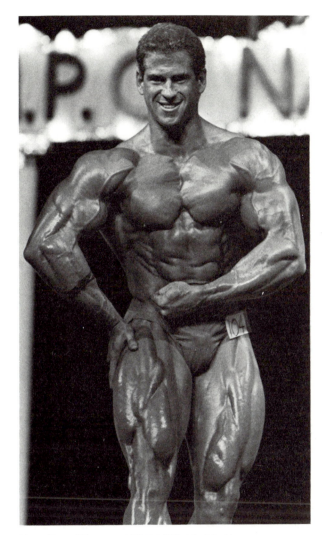

Tom Terwilliger—1985 NPC Light–Heavy Nationals Champ.

generally apply to the super athlete or bodybuilder.

AEROBIC EXERCISES

Plan your aerobics around these types of exercises:

Outdoor Aerobics

Jogging   This is one of the most popular forms of exercise for aerobic condition-

THE GRADUATED JOGGING PLAN

JOGGING SESSION NUMBER	NUMBER OF YARDS JOGGED	NUMBER OF YARDS WALKED
1	440	440
2	550	330
3	660	220
4	770	110
5	880 = ½ mile	440
6	990	330
7	1,100	220
8	1,210	110
9	1,320 = ¾ mile	440

COMMENTS

Continue with the jogging plan as outlined for an additional 36 sessions and you will achieve your goal of jogging 3 miles. This subtle jogging plan will, in most cases, eliminate the possibility of shin splints. Of course this problem will be somewhat dependent upon your jogging surface. Ideally you should jog on a surface (grass, gym floors, sandy beaches) which has some give to it as opposed to such non-give surfaces as asphalt or concrete.

For those of you who are in shape for a maximum jogging effort, you might like this variation: Jog 1½ miles within your limit aerobically then fully extend yourself for a final 1½ miles.

---

ing. The secret to jogging success is to begin gradually and steadily. Those of you who are not really in shape for a maximum jogging session, should consider the graduated jogging plan below, which will help you to get into super aerobic condition.

The Graduated Jogging Plan

The primary goal of this plan is eventually to jog three miles. The graduated jogging plan can be completed in 45 days if you have the stamina and recuperative ability to jog every day. Probably the most sensible approach, however, is to jog every other day until you reach your goal of three miles. Of course this alternative could take you months to complete, but the results will be well worth the effort.

10-Speed Cycling
This exercise expends approximately 300 calories per hour. The gear ratios on the bike afford you the opportunity of selecting your own pedaling intensity. The higher gear ratios will in some cases stimulate extra muscle tissue growth in the thighs. If this is not your desire, then select a lower gear and pedal faster.

Cross-Country Skiing
If you happen to live in an area where you can participate in this aerobic activity, then do so. It is one of the very best aerobic exercises in that it subjects you to the least amount of trauma in the legs and back.

Indoor Aerobic Exercises
Rope Skipping
This is a tremendous exercise and is in fact a favorite of four-time Mr. Universe Bill Pearl. A couple of exercise equipment companies market weighted skip ropes, which offer you the benefit of extra aero-

bic conditioning in the upper torso. Work at doing 70–80 jumps per minute if that allows you to work at your active target heart rate.

Swimming
This is one of the priority exercises in physical therapy sessions. For some individuals, swimming 50 yards per minute results in 14 burned fat calories, and it is stress free on your joints.

Stair Climbing
Climbing 8–10 steps every 5 seconds is very good aerobically, but descending the stairs after reaching the top may not keep your active exercise heart rate up to even its minimum requirement, so monitor this closely.

Minitrampoline
This is a nifty aerobic exercise, and as an added benefit you can do some abdominal crunches while lying on this apparatus. It allows you to really sink into the crunch position, and the extreme tension you are able to apply to the abs in this position is superb.

Jogging in Place
Do this exercise on a soft carpeted area. Gradually work into using wrist and ankle weights as a means by which to increase your aerobic mechanism within the individual muscles of the upper and lower body. For that little extra in the way of abdominal work, bring the knees high into the chest region while forcefully tensing the abs.

Stationary Bicycling
There are many excellent models of these from which to choose, but two that come to mind are the Schwinn Air Dyne and, of course, the Life Cycle, which computerizes

Berry DeMey achieves his dramatic cuts only with proper aerobic training.

all the necessary metabolic factors, such as the pulse rate and oxygen uptake, etc.

The 40/20 Aerobic Squat Program
Initially, this routine requires that you squat with a poundage that is 60 percent of your own body weight. Full-squat one rep every 4 seconds for a 40-second duration. Now rest for 20 seconds while utilizing the Vince Gironda oxygen saturation technique: take 5–10 deep breaths

Rachel McLish—flex appeal.

The 20-Rep Squat
(Deep-Breathing Style)

Select a poundage in this exercise that will seem quite heavy to you on a 10th repetition. Begin your squats by filling the lungs with one deep breath in between repetitions for the first five reps. On repetitions 6–10, breathe deeply twice. Remember that in order to keep the lungs full of air you must always hold your very last breath as you begin your descent on a particular repetition.

When you reach rep 10, you may begin to wonder if you can perform another rep, much less 10 more. At this point, on reps 11–15, you will need to stop and take three deep breaths after each rep. This will give the relaxed muscles a slight rest if the pause is long enough (about 5–10 seconds). This slight rest between reps is used primarily to resummon your mental forces as you psych yourself up for another rep. Rest will occur only in the quads, glutes, and hamstrings. It will not occur in the "anti-gravity" muscles controlling balance, such as the abs, traps, and spinae erectors. Thus you may fail during a set as a result of fatigue in these muscles rather than the prime movers (quads, glutes, hamstrings). On the final five reps, breathe four times between reps.

Always be prepared to help yourself through the "sticking point" of the squat (this can happen anytime between rep 11 and rep 20) by pushing against your thighs with both hands. This can put you in a precarious position if you're attempting these squats with a regular straight exercise bar. The best way to alleviate this problem is to use a cambered squat bar.

You will find that this method of squatting forces cardiovascular development and increases lung capacity. Increased lung capacity suggests rib cage expansion, and this can be accomplished by alternating lightweight stiff-arm

through pursed lips during the 20-second rest pause. The oxygen saturation technique offers some special benefits, such as increased stamina, lower heart rate, and diminished acid levels in the body. Repeat the entire sequence as described above another 19 times for a total of 20 minutes.

breathing pullovers (20–30 reps) with the 20-rep squats. For the purpose of rib cage expansion, you should not use more than a 20-pound bar for the pullover. Anything heavier than this will restrict rib cage expansion. Squat three sets of 20 reps and do three sets of 20–30 reps each of breathing pullovers.

Ask the "golden eagle," Tom Platz, what he thinks of high-rep squats. At one time in his bodybuilding career he was easily able to squat over 400 pounds for more than 20 reps. We encourage you to use this squatting scheme to improve your cardiovascular system.

Nordic Track Cross-country Skiing Exercise
This exerciser affords you all the benefits of regular cross-country skiing, but you don't need any snow. The resistance of this exerciser is proportional to your strength. The erect posture that you assume when using the ski exerciser eliminates knee and high hip joint stress. Position this exerciser at varying degrees of incline for added intensity.

Other Apparatus for Aerobics
Many other exercisers are available for use in your aerobic program. Treadmills are one good choice, as are the various rowing machines. The new computerized rowing machines have a unique mode that lets you row against an imaginary opponent. This could go on forever; we have recommended only a few of the very best, but you should explore other possibilities that appeal to you as well.

John Terilli always warms up before hitting the heavy stuff.

10
MUSCLE INJURIES—CAUSES AND TREATMENT

For bodybuilders who use weight training as a means of acquiring more size and strength, the subject of training injuries deserves immediate attention. Act now to be injury-free for the rest of your life.

The fact is that injuries are a common occurrence in bodybuilding. Consequently, it is highly possible that you will experience some type of muscle injury in your bodybuilding career if you are not careful. Injuries can cut your career short. To prevent that from happening, this chapter is designed to help you become more aware of the causes and types of injuries as well as preventive measures and treatments.

CAUSES OF MUSCLE INJURY

The Fatigue Factor

Workouts that are too long in duration usually are done to perform more sets and/or exercises of an appropriate body part than is necessary in a daily workout program.

The more physically fatigued you become during your workout, the more susceptible you will become to injury. Injury can occur in one or more of the three important muscles (prime movers, synergists, and stabilizers, the primary functions of which are explained in Chapter 4) necessary to the force and stability of exercise movement.

Depending on the body part you happen to be working at a given moment, a prime mover in one exercise may very well be the synergist in another exercise, a stabilizer may become a prime mover, and so forth. The table below shows which muscles take on which of the three functions in some example exercises.

Injury can occur suddenly in an exercise where the prime mover muscle has not yet served in any other capacity in the workout. This can be due in part to using

BODY PART	EXERCISE	PRIME MOVER	SYNERGISTS	STABILIZERS
Mid Pec	Flat Bench	Pectoralis Major	Anterior Delt & Triceps	Hips & Legs
Deltoids	Overhead Press	Anterior Delt	Triceps & Lateral Delt	Hips, Legs, Spinae Erectors
Thighs	Full Squat	Quadriceps & Gluteus Maximus	Spinae Erectors & Hamstrings	Traps & Lats
Lower Back	Prone Hyper-extension	Spinae Erectors	Gluteus & Hamstrings	

Lance Dreher gets a final rep!

inadequate technique; not warming up properly; or, in the case of a specific exercise, going too heavy and placing too much stress either on the muscle belly itself or near the tendon attachments of the muscle.

Injury to a muscle also can occur when the prime mover muscle in one exercise (e.g., overhead press with the anterior delt as prime mover) was functioning earlier in the workout as a synergist (e.g., bench press with anterior delt as synergist). In this case, the anterior delts were already fatigued slightly in the bench press, and by the time overhead presses were begun, fatigue in the delts had accelerated and an injury could result.

Fatigue levels in the muscles accumulate tremendously when they are forced to switch roles from prime mover to synergist, and vice versa, in the same workout. It is therefore of utmost importance that you perform just the right number of sets and exercises for a body part. This factor will naturally be determined by what the majority of bodybuilders have found over the years (through trial and error and scientific research) to be the average number of sets and exercises that excites size and strength with minimal injury.

Fatigue and the Tall Bodybuilder

Fatigue is the tall bodybuilder's training problem. It is a fact that a tall bodybuilder must push or pull the weights over a greater distance than the shorter bodybuilder. As a result, the taller lifter must expend a great deal more energy over a longer period of time, especially near the completion of each rep of a set. Under these conditions injury can occur, and it is very important that the bigger and taller bodybuilders take more time to recover between workouts than the smaller bodybuilders. Taller bodybuilders should follow essentially the same advice as that given to bodybuilders above 35–40 years old; namely, they should take more recovery time between workouts than younger bodybuilders.

Lack of Flexibility

Injury here is caused by forcing a muscle through a range of movement that hasn't been tested previously. Frequently we hear about the injury potential to the knees resulting from squats. It is a fact that squats, when properly performed, actually improve the stability around the knee joints.

The best method for introducing a muscle to a new range of movement is to inch your way gradually into a new depth of movement.

Adding Poundages Too Rapidly

Injuries can result when you add poundages far exceeding those previously used in training. Increase your poundages *slowly*.

Mr. Olympia. Part of his success comes from being injury free throughout his climb to the top.

PUSHING MUSCLES		PULLING MUSCLES
Triceps	versus	Biceps
Anterior Deltoid	versus	Trapezius & Rear Deltoid
Pectoralis	versus	Latissimus Dorsi & Rhomboids
Quadriceps	versus	Hamstrings
	STABILIZE THE BODY	
Spinae Erectors	versus	Abdominals

Unbalanced Strengths

Injury also can result when muscles and supporting strengths are developed unequally. For example, you might injure your lower back while performing some heavy parallel squats because the supporting strength of the lower back is not in proportion to the strength of the thigh muscles. Equal training effort is an absolute requirement for development around the joints of the body, especially since many of these muscles work in pairs, as shown in the table on the preceding page.

Of all the muscle groups depicted in the table above, the two that are most often neglected in training, either separately or as a group, are the quadriceps/ hamstrings and the spinae erectors/abdominals. If you specialize totally in the upper body, you are inviting an injury unless you give equal training to your quads and hamstrings.

In many cases, unless you are into contest training, you may tend to neglect hamstring or leg biceps development. The quadriceps are stronger than the hamstrings in most individuals by a ratio of four to one. Your goal should be to give equal training time to the hamstrings and work at achieving a quad/hamstring strength ratio of three to one. The ultimate would be a two-to-one ratio.

Likewise, lower-body specialists, who train their legs totally while giving little regard to the training of the spinae erec-

Vera Bendel works her delts.

Tom Terwilliger pushes one more rep.

tors and abdominals in the upper body, are headed for some big-time injuries. If you're one of these bodybuilders, you risk blowing out the lower back or groin due to the unbalanced strength ratio between weaker undeveloped erectors/abs and the stronger quad/hamstring muscles.

Similarly, if you train quads/hamstrings and the spinae erectors equally but neglect the abs, or if you neglect the spinae erectors and train the abs, you may be in for some injury problems, especially when it comes to performing *squatting*, *deadlifting*, and *bent-over rowing* types of exercises. To prevent such injuries, train sensibly by applying equal training effort to opposing pairs of the various muscle groups.

Tendon and Ligament Injury

Tendons and ligaments are connective tissues. The tendon attaches muscle to bone, and the ligament connects bone to bone. Tendon and ligament sprains usually occur when a joint is bent farther than its existing range of movement. There are three particular cases in which this can happen:

1. Beginners, who in an overenthusiastic effort overtax their inflexible and previously unused muscles, can suffer strains in the connective tissues of the joints.

2. Advanced bodybuilders can experience the same type of problem, especially

Val Phillips, Canadian champion, gives everything to the lat pulldown exercise.

TREATMENTS AND PREVENTIVE MEASURES

At the first occurrence of an injury it is vitally important that you apply ice packs within the first 10–15 minutes of the injury.

You may decide to use a cold pack made of crushed ice (2–2½ pounds) or the frozen gel pack variety. Regarding the latter, it is important to realize that, depending on the temperature of the freezer unit they're stored in, these gel packs may be many degrees below zero and can cause a mild form of frostbite. Chemical ice packs usually don't keep the injury cold enough for a long enough period. They also have the reputation for causing chemical burns on the body.

Elevate the injured muscle (6–10 inches above the level of your heart) if it is a limb (biceps, triceps, forearm, knee, ankle). Place the ice application on the injured area with an even compression. Secure the ice pack in place with a 6-inch Ace bandage wrap. Ice treatments should be applied for 30–45 minutes at a time, with a 1½- to 2-hour lapse between applications. Repeat this procedure for the first 24 hours after the injury (only during those hours that you are awake) to control swelling. Call a doctor if the pain does not subside.

Whenever the ice pack application is removed, the Ace bandage should be reapplied immediately, and you should wear the wrap during sleeping as well as waking hours. Always make a point to use a sling for arm injuries and crutches for leg injuries, which will help lessen the pain in the injured body part and hasten recuperation. Regular massage between ice applications is also recommended.

After the initial 24 hours of ice ther-

when coming off an extended layoff from training.

3. Lack of flexibility, again, can result in sprain.

Strength in the connective tissue does not increase in proportion to increase in muscle strength. As a result, the connective tissue is very susceptible to injury. Remember this: tendon fibers can take from three to six months to heal at the minor sprain level, and ligaments can take even longer.

Georgia Ann Fudge gets support from her training partner when dumbbell pressing.

Tom Platz gives some friendly advice.

apy, you should begin applying the packs intermittently, along with doing manual massage. When these procedures are not applicable, during times of sleep and work, use an analgesic sports cream or rub on the injury. Along with this therapy it is a good idea to take megadoses of calcium (phosphorus-free), magnesium, and especially manganese, in chelated forms, every three hours for 3–10 days.

Rest for the injured area is of the utmost importance, but this is not to say that you must cease all workout activity. Train around your injury. For example, if you have a shoulder injury, train around this by performing crunches and lying leg raises for the abdominals and leg extensions and leg curls for the quads and hamstrings. Options for the legs include roman chair squats or sissy squats and one-legged squats, all of which can be done with just your own body weight. Do one-arm exercises and movements for the upper body utilizing a Universal machine.

Injuries that do not respond to the treatments suggested above are in need of more intense therapy such as ultrasound and/or diathermy and a good anti-inflammatory agent. If your injury reaches this critical point, you will most definitely want to consult a knowledgeable sports medicine doctor, chiropractor, or physical therapist. These professionals will be of tremendous help to you on your road to recovery by helping you renew flexibility and strengthen the injured muscle.

Some of the very best exercises you can include in your workout program to provide an exceptional degree of stretching and flexibility are full squats, stiff-legged deadlifts (while standing on an exercise bench), shrugs, parallel bar dips, barbell wrist curls (performed on a slight decline), and heel raises.

The most common type of injuries in bodybuilding are to those muscles of the deltoids, triceps, lower back, quads, hamstrings, and knees. These have already been discussed in this chapter. There is, however, one area of the anatomy that deserves additional attention: the elbows. If you're training with sore elbows, follow these guidelines:

Don't . . .
1. perform any type of lockouts or full-extension movements either overhead or in the supine position. This would include the various pressing movements for the chest, deltoids, and triceps.
2. perform any exercises with a wide grip that would cause the elbows to extend away from the sides of the body. This would include exercises like wide-grip bench presses or wide-grip Gironda body drag curls, wide-grip upright rows, etc. Exercises of this nature cause the muscles and tendons to be stretched tight, and this does not assist in the recovery factor of the sore elbows.

Do . . .
1. moves like the pushdowns and dumbbell kickbacks for the triceps, thumbs-up lateral raises for the deltoid.
2. only those exercise movements in which the arms remain close to the sides of the body.

A final note on prevention: the best way to prevent injuries altogether is to follow the *proper* exercise procedure, as detailed throughout this book.

Mike Christian—one of the marvels of modern bodybuilding.

11

THE NUTRIENT FACTOR

Athletes and bodybuilders require certain nutrients, such as carbohydrates, proteins, fats, vitamins, and minerals, as the main source of energy for day-to-day physical activity. It is therefore of the utmost importance that you eat only those foods that will adequately supply these nutrients for the optimum in health, strength, and energy.

NUTRIENTS

It is very important that you understand the basic role of each of these nutrients; the right combinations of them will give you that winning edge in your selected sports performance, especially in bodybuilding.

Carbohydrates

This most valuable nutrient is composed of carbon, hydrogen, and oxygen mole-cules. Combined, they form the various types of sugars and starches needed for fast energy.

Carbohydrates contain approximately four calories per gram of food and should be thought of as a two-part classification consisting of complex and simple carbohydrates.

Upon digestion of a meal, complex carbohydrates begin entering the blood stream as glucose, and for the next several hours they cause a variety of changes in the existing blood sugar levels, which normally range between 10 and 15 grams of blood glucose prior to a meal containing carbohydrates.

These changes include supplying adequate amounts of energy to the brain, to the nervous system, and finally to the muscles. After these initial requirements are met, the body converts the remaining excess glucose into glycogen, which is then stored in the liver and the muscle.

Relatively, the larger the athlete, male

or female, the more blood glucose and glycogen is stored, but these are only minor differences. Due to the fact that complex carbohydrates are assimilated into the bloodstream slowly over a period of several hours, the blood sugar remains at a consistently higher level than normal for an extended period of time. This is important to the sports athlete and bodybuilder because it is blood sugars that determine to some degree existing energy levels.

Complex carbohydrates supply instant energy to the athlete who is participating in moderate athletic endeavors in which the pulse rate is elevated to 120–150 beats per minute. This energy classification also includes those very active levels of physical activity in stop-and-go sports like track and field events (sprinting, jumping, and shot putting), football, regular weight training, powerlifting, and competitive bodybuilding, during which the pulse rate exceeds 150 beats per minute.

The advantages of complex carbohydrates that contain adequate bulk and fiber are numerous:

1. Food items of this nature, in their natural and unrefined state, are usually greater in volume and lower in calories than foods that don't have adequate roughage and fiber, and keep you from overeating because of their bulk. For example, a broiled one-pound sirloin T-bone steak contains approximately 1,848 calories. In order to get the same number of calories from a complex carbohydrate source, such as brown rice, you would have to eat 11 cups, making it virtually impossible to overeat on fibrous bulk.

2. Complex carbohydrates that contain adequate bulk and fiber often contain a percentage of natural and unrefined sugars, and it is because of the bulk and fiber that these sugars are assimilated or introduced into the bloodstream

Mary Roberts—winner of the World Championship.

to a greater extent than if they were ingested in their isolated form. The slower digestive process makes your energy level more consistent.

3. Glucose levels in the body are generally lower than normal in the mornings, upon rising. During those sleeping hours the brain uses up 60 percent of the blood glucose stores. This assumes normal sleeping conditions and does not take into account the various forms of anxiety or stress such as precontest jitters that you may experience during sleep. Such stress will rob the body of even more

energy. Therefore, it is very important to begin each morning with a breakfast containing adequate complex carbohydrates (natural and unrefined), which will slowly begin to raise glucose levels back to normal.

4. Complex carbohydrates containing roughage and fiber aid in the elimination of body waste matter (regular bowel evacuation) and intestinal cleansing.

While the immediate advantages of roughage and fiber are clear, you should be aware that too much roughage and fiber can cause some slight problems such as intestinal gas and in some cases cause water-soluble vitamin (all the B complex vitamins and vitamin C) assimilation problems in the body. Also, some older individuals have experienced mineral deficiencies.

Simple carbohydrates or sugars enter the bloodstream with a rush, which in turn increases your blood sugar level very rapidly, within approximately 20 minutes. The muscles absorb all the blood sugar they can handle, and any excess is stored as fat. All kinds of havoc result from ingesting simple sugars. An hour and a half later, blood sugar and energy levels drop well below the levels they were at before you ingested the simple sugars. Therefore, simple sugars should constitute only a very small percentage of your daily caloric intake, and even then they should be in a natural and unrefined state.

Since complex carbohydrates are the most ready source of energy, particularly in the area of muscle contraction, nutritionists have determined through much research that normal nonathletic individuals should be taking in 50 percent of their daily calories in the form of carbohydrates, with only a very small portion being of the simple sugar variety.

For the active sports athlete or bodybuilder, the daily intake of complex carbo-

John Arnita shows some nice cuts.

hydrates and simple sugar increases to 65 percent of daily calories and can even increase to as much as 70 percent, as would be the case in carbohydrate-loading procedures.

Carbohydrates, in their complex and simple forms, should come from the basic food groups of breads and cereals; vegetables and fruits, including juices; and simple, unrefined sugars. Foods that fall into each category, and the amounts of each that you should eat each day, are listed below. And remember, all carbohydrates should be taken in moderation.

BREAD	CEREALS
Breads and Sweet breads	Natural brown rice (in moderation)
Fruit, Cakes, Rice cakes	Whole grain cereals
Pasta and Spaghetti (made with unbleached whole grains and with no chemicals added)	Bran, Cream of Wheat, Oatmeal, Roman Meal or similar cereal, Sunflower seeds
Whole wheat macaroni	
Buckwheat pancakes Waffles	

Select four or more servings per day from the variety of foods listed in this group. Examples of one serving from the above food groups are as follows:

Breads (various types): 1 slice
Pasta: ½–¾ cup
Waffles: 1 regular
Cereals and rice: ½–¾ cup
Sunflower seeds: 1 ounce

VEGETABLES	FRUITS
Asparagus	Apples
Avocado	Apricots (fresh or dried)
Broccoli	Bananas
Cabbage	Berries (all kinds: blueberries, cranberries, raspberries, strawberries, etc.)
Carrots	
Cucumbers	
Greens (beet tops, spinach, Swiss chard, turnip greens)	Cherries
Green peppers	Citrus fruits (oranges, grapefruits, lemons)
Lettuce (all kinds)	
Onions (green or dry)	Dates
Radishes	Figs
Sweet potatoes	Grapes (all kinds)
Squash (yellow and zucchini in the summer, Acorn and Hubbard in the winter)	Mangoes
	Melons (cantaloupes, honeydews, watermelons)
Spinach	
Tomatoes	Nectarines
White potatoes (baked or boiled and in moderation. There is a lot of sodium in these especially in the skin, though sodium content varies depending on soil conditions.)	Papayas
	Peaches
	Pears
	Pineapples
	Plums
	Prunes (dried or stewed)
	Raisins

Tom Platz—one of the most remarkable and popular physiques on the earth.

VEGETABLE JUICES

Various vegetable juices extacted in their natural state using a juicer such as a Vita Mixer

FRUIT JUICES

Apple juice

Orange juice

Grapefruit juice (unsweetened)

Pineapple juice (unsweetened)

Select four or more servings per day from the variety of foods and juices listed in this food group. Some examples of one serving are as follows:

½ cup of any vegetable

Vegetable and fruit juices: 4 ounces for those weighing 50–125 pounds, 6 ounces for those at 126–165 pounds, 8 ounces for those at 166 pounds and over

1 apple, banana, peach, or pear

Papaya or watermelon: ¾–1 cup

Raisins: 1 ounce

The serving recommendations for the bread and cereal and the vegetable and fruit groups will vary somewhat and depend on the number of complex carbohydrates you require during the day to maintain, lose, or gain body weight. The important thing to remember here is to take in enough of the above-mentioned food group to ensure that you meet the daily caloric percentage, whether you are a nonathlete, a sports athlete, or a body-builder.

THE SIMPLE SUGARS

Raw or dark brown sugar

Natural honey

Maple syrup and maple granules

Unsulphured molasses (assists in the burning of fatty acids in the body)

Rice honey (rice/barley syrup)

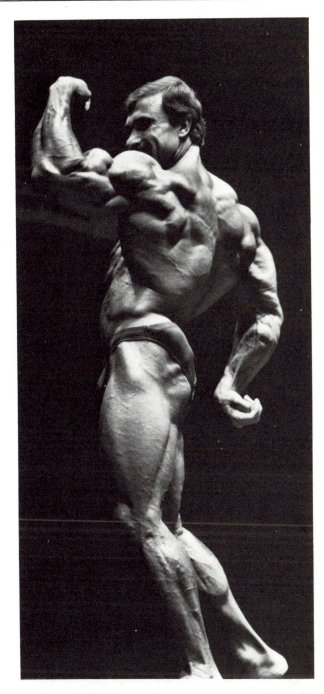

Ali Mala—The Lebanese Superman.

These sugars are classified as simple carbohydrates. Upon digestion they become glucose very quickly and, as a result, cause some rather radical changes in the blood sugar levels. If, in fact, they are used

Sparkling Carolyn Cheshire carries one of the lowest body fat levels in women's bodybuilding today.

in excess, you can expect some type of interference with your protein synthesis

and the utilization (protein metabolism) thereof. The end result is a diminishment of muscular size and strength.

These simple sugars should be used sparingly to prevent any devastating increases in your blood sugar level. A guideline you might want to follow is to begin with 15 percent of your daily complex carbohydrate calorie quota in simple sugars and gradually work up to a maximum of 30 percent in simple sugars.

Proteins

From the nutritional standpoint, proteins could very well be termed muscle-forming foods because one of their primary functions is that of maintenance, repair, and growth of muscle tissue. Proteins also supply energy to the muscles, which in turn contributes to the process of muscle growth, through a muscle chemistry adaptation. During the contraction of selected skeletal muscles, a chemical called *creatine* is formed. This chemical in turn stimulates the muscle to produce the protein molecules *myosin* and *actin*. It is these protein molecules that are responsible for the process of muscle contraction.

While this is a rather brief explanation of muscle chemistry, you can see the importance of protein and how it applies to the size and strength of the skeletal muscles.

Twenty-two amino acids make up the protein molecules. Of these 22, 12 are classified as nonessential, which means that the human body can produce these. The remaining 10 are termed *essential* because the body cannot synthesize them, so they must be extracted from food sources that are called *complete proteins*.

The essential amino acids contained in complete protein food sources are not necessarily in the proper proportion to one another. Their assimilability ratio, or how they function with each other in the

Ulf Larssen of Sweden.

Samir Bannout and his wife, Lori.

body, is the basis for rating complete proteins. Eggs, for example, meet the existing requirements of a complete protein and upon entering the digestive process are assimilated at an astounding 96 percent. It is this nearly perfect food that sets the standard of protein efficiency ratings for all other foods.

Proteins contain approximately the same number of calories per gram of food as the carbohydrates which were discussed previously.

The normal, nonathletic person who does ordinary chores or the person who is in a training layoff should consume ½ gram (2 calories) of complete protein per pound of current body weight, or 17.5 percent of daily calorie needs. The active sports athlete or bodybuilder who is into maintenance bodybuilding (a training mode in which you just hold your existing fitness and strength levels without necessarily making further advances in these areas) should ingest ¾ gram (3 calories) of complete protein per pound of body weight, or 25 percent of daily caloric needs. The same protein requirement applies to those athletes or bodybuilders following the carbohydrate-loading principle. Those who are into heavy training should definitely consider taking in 1 gram (4 calories) of complete protein per pound of body weight, or approximately 33 percent of daily caloric consumption.

Complete proteins are best derived from the basic food groups of dairy products and meats, discussed below.

Dairy Products

Milk is very popular with many athletes because it contains all the essential amino acids and it has a delightful taste when combined with other ingredients for a protein drink. Milk has an assimilability ratio of anywhere from 60 percent to 90 percent, depending on whether the whole milk is pasturized or raw. Raw has the highest ratio.

Milk has been a staple food for many of the top champions in the iron game over the past few decades. Many of these champions attribute a portion of their best gains in size and strength to the use of milk in their diet, and it is not uncommon for them to consume four to six quarts per day during the building-up stage. This may prove to be a bit much for the average sports athlete or bodybuilder, but milk is still a good food to include in your diet.

Some individuals would enjoy the added benefits of milk in their daily diet if it were not for the inability to digest the sugar lactose in the milk. There are a couple of alternatives to this problem. First, you might purchase an over-the-counter lactose enzyme (removes or reduces the lactose in milk) at your local drugstore. The second alternative is to purchase Lactaid, which is a lactose-reduced low-fat milk found at most supermarkets.

A technique that might help is to sip milk very slowly over a period of a half hour per glassful. Why? Milk consumed quickly or gulped down causes the fat content to be digested poorly.

Also, when using milk in a protein drink, avoid using a blender. The rapid whirling action of the blender causes the fat globules in milk to be reduced to a fraction of their normal size, and this causes intolerance to the digestion of milk. A better way to blend milk is to use a shaker container or simply stir in the milk with a spoon. If you must use a blender for mixing milk, blend it in with short bursts of power.

Chemical reactions in milk take place quite rapidly. Within 24 hours after a cow is milked, 10 percent of the vitamin A and 40 percent of the B complex in raw whole

"The Myth."

milk is destroyed. Pasteurization, oxygen, and many other things destroy many of the vitamins and protein in milk.

Eggs are an excellent source of protein and, when combined with milk, make a super complete protein. In fact, when eggs and milk are ingested along with incomplete protein sources, they upgrade the protein efficiency ratio tremendously.

For those of you who are concerned about the cholesterol in eggs, rest assured that there is also a substance known as *lecithin* that aids in the absorption of cholesterol, which can be purchased at your local health food stores.

Natural Ice Cream contains milk and eggs and some sweeteners such as honey. If you follow a healthy diet void of excess sweets, and you don't have any special medical problems (sugar disorders), there is no reason a *moderate* helping of ice cream containing those simple sugars should harm you.

Those of you who have milk allergies might give Tofutti (a nondairy product made with no milk or eggs, but with soy milk, honey, and flavorings, that is virtually free of fat and cholesterol) soybean ice cream a try.

Stay away from commercial ice creams. They are loaded with chemicals that don't do your body any good. Just for starters, there is piperonal, which is used as a vanilla substitute, but its other commercial use is that of louse killer. Or how about diethyl glucol, which is a substitute for eggs but is also used in antifreeze solutions?

Buy only those ice creams that are completely natural. They are very expensive (cost indicators show that a pint of natural ice cream will be in the same range as a half gallon of the common commercial brands) but well worth it.

Other Dairy Products

These include cottage cheese, though this dairy product is high in sodium, at 850 mg per cup, so you should use it in moderation. Other dairy products are yogurt (low-fat) and various cheeses (cheddar, mozzarella, Swiss, etc.).

Daily Servings of Dairy Products

Select three or more servings of dairy products for children, four or more serv-

Ed Corney defies father time.

ings for teenagers, and two or more servings for adults. Examples of one serving of dairy products are as follows:

Cottage Cheese: ½ cup
Various Cheeses: 1 ounce
Ice Cream: ½ cup
Milk: 4 ounces for persons weighing 50–125 pounds, 6 ounces for persons at 126–165 pounds, 8 ounces for persons at 166 pounds and over
Milk Shakes: Same as for milk
Yogurt: 1 cup

Meats

In general, meats have an assimilability ratio of 40 percent. Fish is the easiest meat to assimilate, and pound for pound it contains more protein than any of the other meats listed in this food group.

White fish: This is fish that is less than 2 percent fat, including cod, flounder, haddock, pike, yellow perch, sea bass.

Fat Fish: This is fish that has 2–5 percent fat, including brook trout, mullet, and white perch.

Oily Fish: This is fish that contains 5 percent or more fat, and includes herring, lake trout, salmon, sardines, and tuna. Tuna is an excellent source of protein, but be sure that it is water-packed and sodium-free.

The meats that are the second-easiest to assimilate are those in the poultry category (all domesticated birds that are used for foods):

Chicken
Duck
Fowl
Quail
Squab
Turkey

Beef and lamb are the most difficult of the meats to assimilate. A diet that includes red meats over prolonged periods of time has proven to be very hard on the liver, which has to break down the proteins in the meat, and also on the kidneys, which have to process the waste materials (urea buildup). Red meats cause the liver to overwork due to the fat content and occasional overcooking. This can cause a delay in digestion by as much as 5 hours. Over the long haul, these organs simply cease to function at their maximum capacity.

Again, moderation is the key here. If you must eat red meat, be sure that it is

Rich Gaspari shows his incredible back.

well cooked to destroy the steroids contained within the meat. Also, lean red meats are better than meats that contain a high percentage of fat. Most of the high fat content in meat is impossible to digest because when the fat is cooked (broiling is the preferred method) its composition is altered and the liver cannot synthesize it; the result is a buildup of cholesterol. Speaking of cholesterol, it is interesting to note that an individual's average intake is 450 mg per day, and only half of this is utilized. Also, the body manufactures 700

Mike Christian, U.S.A.

mg of its own cholesterol daily for various body processes, so you should monitor your intake of it carefully.

Eat red meat if you must, but you would be much better off sticking with the lighter meats, such as fish and poultry, and thus increasing your performance in bodybuilding and sports.

Other Proteins

The following proteins are incomplete in nature because they do not include all the essential amino acids. Nonetheless, they are an important addition to your diet, especially when combined with the best of the complete proteins, milk and eggs. The incomplete proteins are derived from veg-

Brian Homka helps Scott Wilson with a press.

etables and include beans, lentils, peas, and nuts (all kinds, including natural old-fashioned peanut butter). For more complete information on nutritional subjects such as cholesterol, subscribe to *The Health Letter* (P.O. Box 326, San Antonio, Texas 78292) published twice monthly

A food item is a protein if it contains 15 percent or more protein, and the above vegetable sources meet this standard. But because certain essential amino acids are absent from *all* vegetables, it is very important to combine them with natural cereal, grains, and breads. This practice will certainly upgrade the amino acid content of these foods. Here are some sample combinations:

Beans and cornbread
Lentil soup and whole wheat bread
Brown rice and bean casserole
Beans and tortillas
Tortillas and natural peanut butter
Refried beans and rice

If you are interested in exploring the merits of combining legumes (beans, lentils, peanuts, peas, and soybeans), cereal/grains, and seeds (sunflower, pumpkin, etc.), we suggest you purchase a good vegetarian cookbook.

Daily Servings of Meat and Vegetable Proteins
Select two or more servings daily for all individuals. Examples of one serving from the meat and vegetable (legumes) protein groups are:

2–3 ounces of fish, poultry, pork, beef, or lamb
Canned tuna: ½–¾ cup
Cooked legumes: 1 cup
Peanut butter: 4 tablespoons

Fats and Oils

The final food group that must be addressed is that of fats and oils. Certain

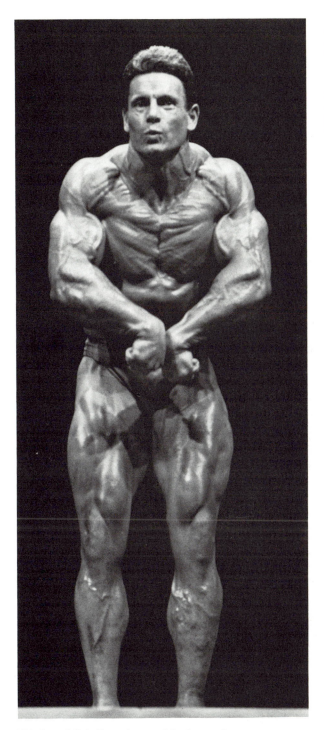

Walter O'Malley shows his ripped pecs.

select fats are an integral part of good, sound nutrition. They are one of the most abundant sources of vitamins A, D, E, and

187

K. Fats also supply the body with energy during those periods of inactivity (sedentary states) or rest and also during aerobic-oriented activities. It is during those times that the body will burn 50–70 percent fatty acids as an energy source.

Fatty acids contain chains of carbon atoms. The carbon atoms in turn have spaces available in which hydrogen atoms can attach themselves. Simply stated, if all of the available spaces in the carbon atom are occupied by hydrogen atoms, the fatty acid is determined to be a saturated fatty acid. This is one of the least desired fatty acids due to the fact that the molecules become very hard and do not combine with other substances in the bloodstream. The end result is clogged arteries, which can lead to a number of health problems.

Beef fat, for example, contains approximately 50 percent saturated fatty acids, so it is best to eat beef only in its lean state and in moderation. Peanut butter is another example. When you read the label on a jar of commercial peanut butter, you will notice the word *hydrogenation*, which means that the empty spaces in the carbon atoms have been filled by hydrogen. Stay away from peanut butter that includes this listing and go for the brands that are labeled *old-fashioned*. Look for *hydrogenation* on food labels as well. Cooking oils, for example, that list *hydrogenation* or *hardening* on the labels should *not* be included in your diet.

The fatty acid that *should* be a part of your daily diet is of the *unsaturated* variety. An unsaturated fatty acid has spaces in the carbon atom that are not occupied by hydrogen atoms. These fatty acids combine remarkably well with other substances in the bloodstream and do not clog the arteries. They are derived from certain items in the dairy products group and the vegetable and cereal food groups,

Richard Roy.

and there are also the unsaturated fatty acids found in fish. Everyone needs this type of fatty acid for good health, and competitive bodybuilders in particular need them in order to acquire those diamond-hard cuts.

Fats contain nine calories per gram of food, which is just about twice the calories contained in a gram of protein or carbohydrate. Average nonathletes will be taking in approximately 32.5 percent of their daily calories in the form of unsaturated fats. (This percentage is below the common 45 percent daily fat intake that most individuals subscribe to. It would be a good idea to reduce this percentage to what the American Medical Association recommends, which is 23 percent.) Active sports athletes and bodybuilders should not take in more than 5–10 percent of their daily calories in the form of unsaturated fats, and this includes those athletes following carbohydrate-loading procedures.

Since the fat you need usually can be gleaned from the foods discussed earlier, you generally won't have to make a con-

The scintillating Gladys Portugues of New York City.

centrated effort to eat enough fat. There are, however, times when a concentrated fat source is desirable in terms of taste, such as when you want to spread a pat of butter on whole wheat toast. In such cases, the fat should be extracted from natural and unrefined items such as certified raw butter and cream, olive oil, peanut oil, sesame oil, dairy sour cream, soybean oil, sunflower seed oil, and unsaturated vegetable oils. Remember, whenever possible substitute unsaturated fat for saturated fats. You'll feel healthy and take another positive step toward your goal of optimum muscle-building nutrition.

FOODS TO AVOID

AVOID THESE FOODS	REASONS TO AVOID	SUBSTITUTES
Commercial candies	Concentrated sugars	Dried fruit candies
Chocolate products	Concentrated sugars	Carob and Cara Coa
Commercial cereals	Excess sugar/salt; presweetened with white sugar and synthetic glucose.	NATURAL CEREALS such as 100% Bran (Kellogg's or Nabisco), buckwheat, cracked wheat, Cream of Wheat, Farina, Lorma Linda products, bulk bin grains and granola
		NOTE: Soak all natural grains overnight in distilled water (less salt) to expand the grain to its maximum or original size. This helps to eliminate gas and gas pains.
Canned Fruits	Loaded with excess sugars and heavy syrups.	Canned fruits packed in natural juices or water
Desserts and pastries (butterhorns, cakes, cookies, cheesecakes, creampuffs, doughnuts, Twinkies (fluffed lard), sweet rolls)	Excess sugar and white flour	Same as for commercial candies and of course fresh fruits
Ice cream products	Excess sugar and chemicals	Tofutti (nondairy product) ice cream, natural ice creams, blender drinks listed in this book
Items labeled juice drinks, Soda pop, and even those labeled as diet	Loaded with sugar. Soda pop contains excess sugars (12 teaspoons per 12-ounce can). Diet colas contain excess sodium.	Drink matural bottled juices such as those marketed by Mission San Juan.
White sugars	Bleached in sulphuric acid, is mucus-forming, and accelerates mineral loss	Simple sugars listed earlier in this chapter
White flour products such as breads, macaroni, muffins, rolls, spaghetti, etc.	Contains "empty calories" due to lack of many of the 40 nutrients the body needs daily. They also contain mucus-forming white	Whole wheat flour products

flour and are usually bleached, chemically treated, and synthetically fortified.

Butter substitutes (margarines) and prepared hydrogenated fats	Cause a cholesterol buildup	Butter, soybean oil, vegetable oils
Coffee	Causes fluctuating blood sugar levels, which in turn results in overeating. Loaded with caffeine, which can interfere with certain vitamin nutrient assimilation by up to 45 percent.	Limit this caffeinated beverage to 2 cups a day. Do this slowly over a period of 4-5 weeks to give your body a chance to accept the change. Use Kero, Pioneer, or Postum and percolate it fresh.
Tea	Contains caffeine and tannic acid and causes some of the same problems as coffee.	Good tea substitutes include alfalfa, herbal, mint, peppermint (all caffeine-free).

Juliette Bergman performs an incline press for her chest.

Alcoholic beverages (beer and wine, etc.)	Alcohol anesthetizes the stomach lining, causing overeating. Also, excess alcohol consumption during air travel causes dehydration. Finally, when alcohol is combined with a meal, the alcoholic calories will be used as an energy source first and other food calories will be stored as fat.	After having read the reasons to avoid alcohol, you and you alone must decide on an appropriate substitute.
Sharp spices, mustard, pickles, and various rich sauces	Irritate the stomach lining and also interfere with the digestive juices	Herbal spices
Corn curls, potato chips, etc.	Excess saturated fats and sodium.	Low-fat and low-sodium brands from a health food store or health food section in a grocery store

Look at the wings of Mike Christian.

Pork products (bacon, ham, sausage links) and cold cuts	Pork products are loaded with sodium and also release energy so quickly that the protein in the food can't be fully utilized, resulting in overworked kidneys and toxins spilling over into the blood. Deli meats contain excess chemicals such as nitrites and nitrates. Avoid any meat that has been cured, pickled, preserved, salted, smoked, or spiced.	Health food store brands such as Lorma Linda and Worthington products.
Commercial airline food	Loaded with sodium. Competitive bodybuilders should stay away from these meals.	If it's a long flight and you must eat, prepare your own travel foods ahead of time
Fast-food restaurants	Same basic problem as the airline foods, as well as excess fat and empty calories.	Head for the salad bar.
Table salt	There are numerous reasons for avoiding this substance. Most important to the athlete, salt is a water retainer. One extra teaspoon of table salt can cause a retention of as much as ½ pound of water.	Dulse, Irish moss (carrageen), kelp powder
Canned vegetables	Loaded with salt and sugar. As an example, a 3½-ounce can of processed peas contains 236 milligrams of salt, while 3½-ounces of fresh garden peas have only 2 milligrams of salt.	Health food store low-sodium vegetables or vegetables from the vegetables and fruits group listed earlier in this chapter.
Chemical laxatives (Lasix, etc.)	Damage to the intestinal tract and a cause of loss of potassium	Use only natural and organic diuretics. One of the best is cucumbers and its juices. Also make use of pitted prunes or unsweetened prune juice (4- or 8-ounce glass). Try natural bran and work up to 2-3 teaspoons per meal. Perform an enema as a final alternative to the above. Suspend water bottle (use tepid to warm water) two feet off floor. Introduce water slowly. Hold for 10-15 min. Repeat sequence two more times. Replace evident electrolyte (body mineral) loss with items like bananas, mineral supplementation, yogurts, etc.

Commercial salad dressings and sandwich spreads	Contain sugar and salt and include a food additive that inhibits the use of iron and causes hunger.	Oil and vinegar and lemon juice
Canned meats packed in oil (including fish products like tuna, sardines, etc.)	Too much oil (excess calories)	Water-packed variety

Many of the foods to avoid listed in the table obviously contain excessive amounts of processed sugars and sodium or a combination of both. Some of them also contain empty calories, meaning that they lack sufficient quantities of the 40-plus nutrients that the human body demands on a daily basis. To compound these problems, over 3,000 additives are used in the huge selection of commercially processed packaged foods and farm products available to us. As a result of these additives, the average American consumes over 4 pounds of chemicals in his or her diet each year. *Read the labels* on the food items you purchase because this will help you become more nutritionally conscious of the types of foods you are putting into your body.

A SECRET FOR DETERMINING FOOD TOXICITY

Take your pulse rate 30 minutes prior to eating a meal, then three more times 30 minutes apart, beginning with the commencement of the meal. If your pulse has not increased more than 10 beats per minute, then the meal is nontoxic to your digestive system. If your pulse has increased more than 15 beats, avoid those foods in the future. Since you probably will be eating from all basic food groups at each meal, it may take a little trial and error to identify the exact toxic food. In

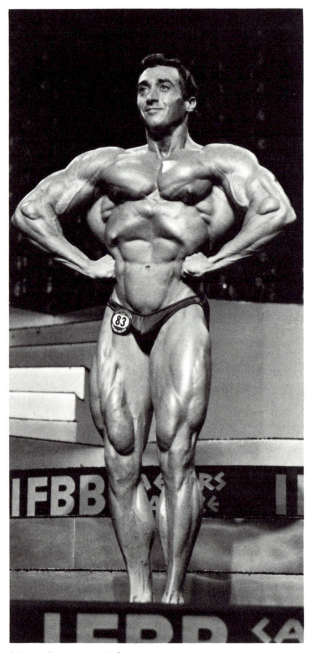

Marc Botduc of Canada.

Britain's Frank Richards shows the audience an impressive most muscular.

COOKING METHODS TO AVOID

Deep-fried fish and fried beef (hamburger, steak)	Overcooking, as in the method of frying, alters the fat content to such a degree that it can't be properly metabolized into the bloodstream and as a result forms plaque on the arterial walls.	Bake or broil. In the case of light fish such as halibut, steaming is an appropriate cooking method.
Fried eggs	See above	Poach, hard-boil, or soft-boil. For those of you who like raw eggs but don't like the idea of the avidin in the raw egg and its destruction of the B vitamin biotin, simply boil the egg for 10 seconds and no more to counteract this problem.

THE $1,000 SECRET

For those of you who have difficulty swallowing raw eggs, here is a unique way of chugging them down: Set out 2 small drinking glasses (shot glass variety). Drop 1 or 2 yolks into one glass. Fill the other glass with mineral water. Now chug the raw egg yolks. Immediately drink the mineral water to wash the taste away.

What to do with the egg whites? Simply soft-boil the egg whites and, after boiling, combine with fresh strawberries for a low-cal protein dessert.

Boiled vegetables	Loss of vital nutrients	It is better to eat vegetables in their raw state, but not every time. Too much of even a good thing can cause problems. Too many raw vegetables can irritate the intestinal tract due to the coarseness of the cellulose fiber. It is a good method to steam vegetables to break down the fiber content somewhat. Dinner is a good time to do this since the digestive process is beginning to slow down. Use stainless steel cookware.

other words, you may have to eliminate one food at a time to pinpoint the item that is toxic to you.

VITAMINS, MINERALS, AND OTHER SUPPLEMENTS

Vitamins and minerals are a necessary part of the diet for obtaining optimum physical condition. We are talking about 100 percent natural vitamins and minerals, not those of the synthetic variety. Numerous published studies conclude that synthetic vitamins and minerals are in no way as potent or beneficial as those that are totally natural.

Many dietary food supplements are available in the form of vitamin and mineral packs for both the male and female bodybuilder. If you were to try to obtain all the necessary vitamins and minerals simply by following a sound daily diet, your caloric intake would exceed your daily total energy expenditure, and the end result would be a gain in body fat.

Vitamins and minerals are often prescribed *individually*. When this is the case, you must realize that they need to be taken in certain proportions in order to be effective. For example, when one particular vitamin or mineral is taken excessively, it can cause a serious deficiency in other existing vitamins and minerals in our system because it uses them up and their value is lost.

When you are comparing brand names, always look for a *certification* of quality. This is simply a guarantee that the ingredients in the products are of the highest quality obtainable and that all coated tablets consist of a vegetable protein coating and contain no sugar, starch, artificial flavorings or colors, or coal tar derivatives.

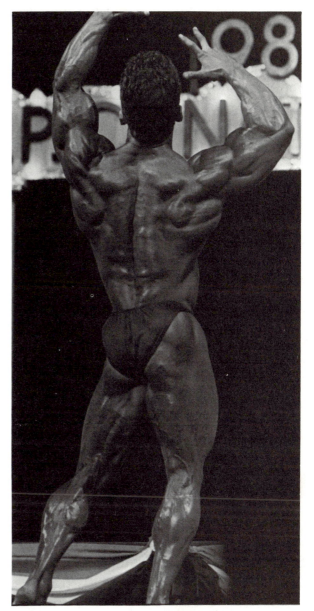

Sensational Lee Labrada—IFBB World Champion.

We won't go into depth here on the subject of vitamins and minerals since thousands of books and scientific papers have been written exclusively on this subject, but we do want to make a few comments.

1. Always read the labels that accompany the individually bottled vitamins and minerals and/or the dietary food sup-

plement packs. Some of the dosages are measured in micrograms (mcg) and some in milligrams (mg), so don't confuse these two measurements.

1 microgram = 1/1,000,000 gram
1,000 micrograms = 1 milligram (mg)
1 milligram (mg) = 1/1,000 gram
1,000 milligrams = 1 gram

2. To give you the greatest benefits, vitamins and minerals must work synergistically (jointly or together), according to the following ratios.

- Take five parts vitamin A to one part vitamin E.
- All of the important B vitamins should be taken in exact proportion to one another. For example, if you take 50 mg of vitamin B_1, you must take the same amount of B_2, B_6, and B_{12}.
- Take two parts phosphorus-free calcium to one part magnesium (helps eliminate constipation). If this ratio is not met, the magnesium will draw calcium out of the bones.

3. Vitamins need time to be assimilated into your body's system, yet occasionally vitamins can be flushed out of your system before they are fully absorbed. The greatest flusher of the B vitamins and vitamin C is water. These vitamins are extremely water-soluble, and excessive drinking of water and juices seems to flush the water-soluble vitamins from the system. (Normal daily water consumption is 1 ounce for every 2 pounds of body weight. For example, if you weigh 160 pounds, you should be drinking 80 ounces of water daily, or 10 8-ounce glasses.) It is recommended that you take your B and C vitamins and your calcium about 30 minutes before eating a meal. Take all other vitamins and minerals with or directly after a meal.

Rather than prescribing certain dos-ages of vitamins and minerals, I would suggest that you purchase a good dietary food supplement pack. These packs contain all the necessary vitamins and minerals to get the male or female athlete through a tough workout or a stress-filled business day. Best of all, they're time-released, so that the essence of the vitamin pills is released over several hours after consumption.

Guide to Purchasing a Food Supplement Pack

Make sure the vitamins and minerals you take meet these criteria:

- 100-percent natural
- have certification of quality
- meet the ratio quotas discussed above

If you are now taking your vitamins individually, and they are not of the time-released variety, you may find it to your advantage to divide your daily dosage in two and take half at 8:00 A.M. and half at 6:00 P.M.

VITAMIN CHART

VITAMIN A

FUNCTIONS:
1— Promotes tissue formation.
2— Increases blood platelets.
3— Promotes growth and feeling of well-being.
4— Promotes appetite and digestion, especially in children.
5— Essential to the health and integrity of epithelial tissue and its resistance to infection, notably of eyes, tonsils, sinuses, air passages, lungs, and gastrointestinal tract.

MOST RELIABLE SOURCES:
Whole milk, butter, cheese, egg yolk, cod liver oil, thin green leafy vegetables, yellow corn, yellow sweet potatoes, carrots, spinach, green beans, peas, bananas and fish oils.

Massive Lee Haney gives thanks after winning his second Olympia.

VITAMIN B

All cooked foods are deficient in this nerve- and brain-nourishing element depending on the degree of heat and the time the food is exposed to the heat.

FUNCTIONS:

1— Increases appetite.

2— Promotes digestion.

3— Promotes growth by stimulating metabolic processes.

4— Protects body from certain nerve and brain diseases.

5— Increases quantity and improves quality of

milk during lactation. Mothers who do not have enough milk usually lack vitamin B.

6— Stimulates pancreatic secretions, including insulin.

7— Necessary to maintenance of thyroid and adrenal glands.

8— Necessary to normal function of anterior pituitary.

MOST RELIABLE SOURCES:

Whole grain cereals, peas, beans, raw fruits, buttermilk, corn, cabbage, spinach, egg yolk, honey, and yeast, specifically dried yeast, & brewer's yeast

VITAMIN C

FUNCTIONS:

1— Essential to the health and integrity of endothelial tissues.

2— Cooperates with B in nutrition of thyroadrenal system.

3— Is essential to oxygen metabolism.

4— Cooperates with D in regulation of calcium metabolism.

5— Promotes leucocytic and phagocytic activity.

MOST RELIABLE SOURCES:

Green peppers, oranges, lemons, tomatoes (raw or canned; without the addition of soda) bananas and other raw fruits, sprouted grains, green leafy vegetables, potatoes, unpasteurized milk, liver, and raw cabbage.

Vitamin C is not stored in the body. A fresh supply must be had every day.

VITAMIN D

FUNCTIONS:

1— Controls calcium equilibrium and regulates mineral metabolism.

MOST RELIABLE SOURCES:

Cod liver oil and other fish oils, egg yolk, whole milk, and spinach. Exposure of naked skin to sunshine or ultraviolet light. Few foods contain vitamin D. Nature expects the animal to get this vitamin from the sunshine by the short wavelength rays changing the ergosterol in the skin into vitamin D.

VITAMIN E

FUNCTIONS:

1— Necessary to reproduction in both male and female.

2— Probably concerned in the metabolism of calcium and magnesium by increasing their diffusibility in the tissue fluids and increasing the mineral nutrition to the nervous and muscular tissues. This action also prevents the formation of calcium deposits in blood vessel walls, tendency to arterial hypertension, and loss of mobility of eye lens.

MOST RELIABLE SOURCES:

Whole grain cereals (whole wheat, whole corn, etc.), milk, lettuce, watercress, and raw fruits.

VITAMIN F

(A Growth Factor of Our Own Designation.)

FUNCTIONS:

1— Promotes growth.

2— Concerned with calcium metabolism. Reduces serum calcium, cooperates with vitamin D if both are present, but aggravates rickets if the supply of D is deficient.

3— Aids in anemic conditions of deficiency origin.

4— Improves skin color and circulation.

MOST RELIABLE SOURCES:

Associated with E in some cereals — oats and rye in particular. Probably present in milk and cod liver oil and responsible for the greatly reduced toxicity of the vitamin D content of cod liver oil over the synthetic vitamin.

VITAMIN G

FUNCTIONS:

1— Necessary to growth and development.

2— Necessary to normal calcium metabolism and erythrocyte formation.

MOST RELIABLE SOURCES:

Cereal germ, brewer's yeast, eggs.

Other Supplements

Amino Acids   Eating natural foods that contain sufficient complete protein can be costly, so you should consider amino acid supplementation. Amino acid supplementation helps the body function at peak performance by ensuring that the amino acids' crucial functions are carried out. Those functions include:

- aiding in the reduction of body fat levels
- stabilizing blood sugar levels, which in turn reduces one's appetite
- aiding in cardiovascular endurance
- helping maintain a positive nitrogen balance in the body, which helps maintain the pumped-up feeling in the muscle
- aiding in the repair of broken-down muscle tissue, which means accelerated recuperation
- helping increase muscle size and strength for faster gains

If you desire the optimum in peak performance, then you should definitely consider adding a complete amino acid supplement to your daily diet.

General Recommendations   Take 3–10 tablets three to four times a day. The number of grams you receive from these tablets will vary depending on which ones you buy.

Left to right: Ben Herder, Holland; Mohamed Makkawy, Canada; and Albert Beckles, Britain.

Amino acid levels exist in the bloodstream at about 30–40 grams for three to four hours, so 3–10 tablets four times a day would be an excellent way of getting a portion of your daily protein requirement.

Then, of course, there are those times when you will need a little extra in the way of protein or amino acid compounds, such as during cold weather conditions.

Always take the amino acid tablets between meals or after a workout while using a form of complex carbohydrate (e.g., apple) as a carrier.

Amino Acid Guidelines

1. Take your complete amino acid combinations as instructed above.

2. Isolated amino acids should not be taken at the same time as the complete amino acids. There should be a two-hour time lapse between these two, or the special functions of the isolated aminos will become ineffective.

3. The isolated amino acids 1-arginine and 1-ornithine should be taken in a ratio of two to one and are conveniently marketed as such. They will trigger the release of growth hormones (increased muscle size) from the pituitary gland (this gland is found at the base of the brain and through hormone release is responsible for metabolic rate, growth rate, and electrolyte balance). These two isolated amino acids also assist in burning fat. For best results, take these isolated amino acid forms half an hour before retiring for the night, because the pituitary gland will begin to release the growth hormones in as little as one hour into sleep.

4. The above isolated amino acids should never be taken with a concentrated sugar drink because simple sugars interfere with the functioning capacity of the amino acids. Natural apple juice is a good choice.

5. The amino acid 1-phenylalanine

Ulf Larssen, Sweden.

should be taken half an hour before meals and has proven to be an efficient hunger suppressant, which is naturally a very important consideration for those desiring to lose body fat. Best of all, you don't build up any tolerances to this natural amino acid, so its effectiveness is indefinite in duration.

6. Some individuals may experience some form of side effect or toxic reaction to amino acids. If you notice reactions such as nervousness, profuse sweating, or sleeplessness while taking the amino acid supplements, it would be wise to back off the recommended dosages somewhat. Also, when you are bedridden due to illness or in an immovable state, the body's ability to assimilate protein (amino acids) decreases, so your daily allowance of proteins should not exceed this guideline: multiply your body weight in pounds by .36 grams. For example, if you are a woman and you weigh 100 pounds, you should be taking in 36 grams (1 gram of protein equals 4 calories) or 144 calories of protein each day that you are bedridden or immovable. Obviously, this condition will require you to make some adjust-

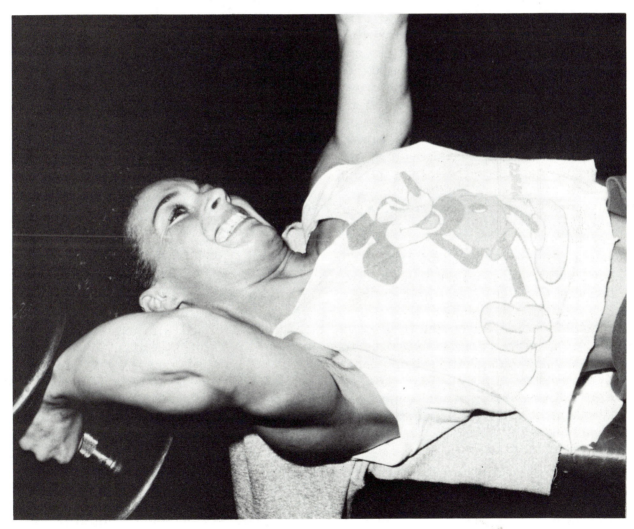

Alternate biceps stretch performed by Erika Mes.

ments in your ratios of carbs and fats as well, which is only natural since your activity levels have decreased radically.

7. Another way to maintain proper protein levels in the body is to use a blender drink containing around 30 grams of a good milk and egg protein powder. Always be sure to check the amino acid mix of your powders. While milk and egg powders are the very best, there are also some vegetable-source protein powders. However, they lack certain amino acids, which have to be made up from other sources.

Desiccated Beef Liver Extracts

Another unique method for maintaining proper protein levels in the body comes from the iron guru, Vince Gironda. He recommends that his students take two desiccated beef liver tablets (imported Argentinian) of 21 grains (1.5 grams each) every waking hour of the day. This practice has a couple of special benefits: an improved pump in the body part during workouts and, report some students, a one-inch gain in arm measurement after two weeks of using this formula.

Bromelain/Papain Digestive Enzymes

These tablets should be used as directed to assist in the digestion of your meals.

The Fat Burners—Choline and Inositol

Choline and inositol are isolated forms of the B complex vitamins and are lipotropic (fat emulsifiers) in nature. Take these in the ratio of two parts choline to one part inositol. Begin with 500 mg of choline to 250 mg of inositol. Gradually work up to a 2,000 mg to 1,000 mg ratio.

Kelp and Alfalfa

This combination seems to have a natural anabolic effect on the body, which is certainly great news.

DIGESTION FREQUENCY

Muscles that are being subjected to vigorous workouts need an increased supply of blood, which brings in more oxygen and energy substrate compounds (glucose, glycogen, etc.) to the muscle and speeds up the elimination of waste products.

Research indicates that this extra blood supply comes directly from the digestive organs. Looking into the digestive process, we find that solid and semisolid foods travel from the mouth to the stomach in approximately seven seconds. Liquids pass from the mouth to the stomach in less than a second.

As soon as food enters the stomach, gastric juices are released and set into motion peristaltic movements (successive waves of involuntary contractions that pass along the walls of the intestines and the internal muscular structure, breaking food into smaller particles and finally into semiliquid, which is then moved onward into the intestines). During the process of digestion, these foods undergo a further chemical change that enables them to be absorbed through the walls of the intestines. This particular chemical change transforms the food particles into a liquid form. The vast circulation system of the body picks up this material and supplies the billions of cells in the body with new protoplasm. This is known as *assimilation*, and it causes new cells to form; thus growth occurs.

Pure liquids pass from the stomach into the intestines within minutes. Carbohydrates are the first of the solid foods to move into the intestines, while proteins require a bit longer in the digestive process. Fats are the slowest to digest. An average meal may take anywhere from three to five hours to digest, although this depends on the composition of the foods

Jusup Wilcosz awaits the judges' decision.

eaten. Meals comprised entirely of carbo-hydrates will digest more quickly than an entire protein meal. Fatty foods require the maximum amount of time for proper digestion.

The proportions of each of these major food sources affect the duration of digestion. Ideally, you should allow three hours to elapse after eating an average meal consisting of carbohydrates, proteins, and minimal fats before beginning a workout session. Why? Because if you begin to exercise on a full stomach, the blood in the stomach will be directed to the active muscle, and proper digestion of the food will be suspended. This action will result in partially digested foods that will stagnate or ferment. A rupture or hernia then becomes a very real possibility due to the extreme pressures of the undigested foods against the abdominal walls during strenuous exertion.

THE 4-TO-6-MEALS-A-DAY DIET OUTLINE

The goal of this diet outline is to maintain your current body weight on a constant and consistent daily basis. It is also very expandable in that it can be used as a plan for those wishing to *lose* body fat or *gain* extra muscle mass. Simply add or subtract certain foods to fit your daily caloric needs in these areas.

The four-to-six-meals-a-day diet (consisting of smaller feedings) allows the body better metabolization of your foods as opposed to overloading the stomach and digestive process on just three large daily meals.

Throughout this chapter we have stressed the importance of eating the

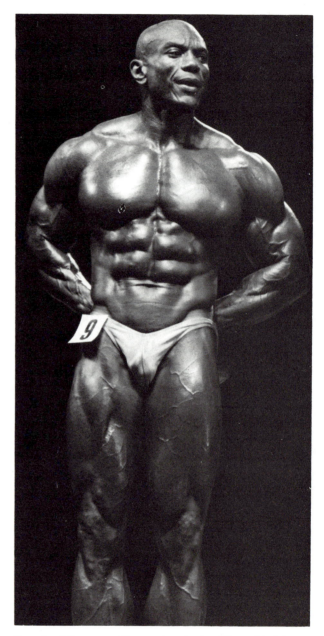

Sergio Oliva continues to do battle with his massive muscularity.

proper ratio of complex carbohydrates, complete proteins, and unsaturated fats. These ratios are summarized in the following chart.

DAILY CALORIE PERCENTAGE

	CARBOHYDRATES (%)	PROTEINS (%)	FATS (%)
Nonathlete	50	17.5	32.5
Bodybuilders and Sports Athletes (maintenance training)	60-65	25-30	5-10-15
Bodybuilders and Powerlifters (in hard training)	45-47	33-35	15
Endurance Athletes (carb loading only)	70	25	5

For example, if your daily energy count is 3,410 calories, and you are a bodybuilder into maintenance training, 60 percent of your daily calories should come from complex carbs. This amounts to 2,046 calories. Twenty-five percent of your daily calorie consumption should come from complete proteins, which amounts to 852.5 calories. Sound nutrition always includes some form of unsaturated fats. Since you've used up 85 percent of your daily calories on carbohydrates and proteins, you have 15 percent left over, and this percentage should come from unsaturated fats. In our 3,410-calorie example, fats should account for 511.5 calories.

Meal Guidelines

Breakfast

For each meal or snack, accompany the food with the beverage of your choice.

Option No. 1

Omelette, made with 4–5 eggs, cheese, tomatoes

1 whole papaya

Chopped fresh pineapple

Three-grain cereal (brown rice, buckwheat, and millet) with a pat of butter

Bring the cereal to a boil and then let it simmer for 10 minutes. Take it off the stove and let it sit until all the moisture is absorbed. Add a pat of butter.

The star of muscle—Rich Gaspari.

Option No. 2
Fresh strawberries topped with certified raw cream and a dash of honey
4–5 fertile eggs, scrambled in raw butter
1–2 slices flourless whole grain bread with a pat of butter

Option No. 3: Dieter's Delight
2–3 scoops low-fat cottage cheese

Walnuts and sunflower seeds with honey or almonds and pecans
1 bunch seedless grapes

Refer to Barbara Kraus's *Calories and Carbohydrates.*

Option No. 4
Old-fashioned cooked oatmeal
½ cup diced dates

Jeff Williams, U.S.A.

½ cup dairy cream
Honey and wheat germ flakes

Five minutes before the oatmeal is finished, add the dates and cream and blend. Top with honey and wheat germ flakes.

Option No. 5
Whole brown rice, cooked
½ cup raisins
½ cup dairy cream
Honey and wheat germ flakes

Five minutes before rice is cooked, blend in raisins and cream. Top with honey and wheat germ.

Option No. 6
Big bowl sliced bananas
½ cup chopped dates
½ cup raisins and figs
Honey and cream

Mix all ingredients together.

Mid-Morning Snack (2-3 hours after breakfast)

1-2 pieces fresh fruit *or* a nutritional drink like the Postworkout Drink in Chapter 18 *or* a regular serving of yogurt

Lunch (2 hours after snack)
Option No. 1
½ pound fresh fish
Tossed green salad
2 hard-boiled eggs
1 orange

Option No. 2
1 cup low-fat cottage cheese
Omelette, made with 2-3 eggs, melted cheese, and chopped onions and tomatoes folded in

1 fresh vegetable or 1 full slice watermelon
1 8-ounce glass apple juice

Mid-Afternoon Snack (2½ hours after lunch)

1 cheese or meat sandwich on whole wheat bread
Beverage of your choice

Dinner (3½ hours after snack)
Option No. 1
Large serving of chicken, fish, or steak
Large tossed green salad (alfalfa sprouts, sliced cucumbers, lettuce, and radishes sprinkled with sesame seeds and sunflower seeds and topped with a mixture of lemon juice, olive oil, and vinegar
Baked potato or some brown rice

Option No. 2
½-pound ground beef patty *or* ⅓ pound liver
1 glass tomato juice
1-2 pieces cheese (cheddar or other natural cheese)
1 piece fruit (1 cantaloupe, or 1 banana, sliced), with cream poured over and a trace of honey

Bedtime Snack (2-3 hours after dinner)
Have this snack no later than 8:00 P.M. if you are on a weight loss program.

3-4 slices cheese *or* 1-2 pieces fresh fruit *or* popcorn

You can have as much popcorn as you can eat. Go easy on the salt, but use some butter. For an extra treat, lightly sprinkle on some Parmesan cheese. Drink some grapefruit juice along with your popcorn.

Mohamed Makkawy.

12
ESTIMATING YOUR ENERGY EXPENDITURE

To maintain your present body weight, neither gaining nor losing weight, a male bodybuilder will have to take in 12 times his weight in pounds in calories per day, while a female bodybuilder should take in 11 times her body weight in calories per day.

This is the basal metabolic rate (BMR) or the normal speed at which the body burns calories when at rest to provide its basic energy needs. The figures cited above do not take into account any of your daily physical activity expenditures.

As might be expected, energy requirements vary somewhat from individual to individual, depending on gender, body size in area, present height, and current body weight.

A basic formula for determining ideal body weight as it corresponds to height is as follows:

Base Figure
Female—5 feet, 100 pounds
For every ½ inch in height over this base figure, add 2¾ pounds. For each full inch, add 5½ pounds.
Male—5 feet, 110 pounds
Add 5 pounds for each ½ inch over the base figure or 10 pounds for each additional full inch.

Most such formulas are derived mathematically, and the approximations and individual differences will vary—often enormously—from accurate assessments. To determine your ideal body weight and muscle measurements more accurately, consult the charts at the end of this chapter.

There are no absolutes for estimating your daily energy expenditures according to your lifestyle activities (job classifications, recreational periods, and workouts, etc.), beyond your basal metabolic rate (BMR).

A "guestimate" based on the average person's daily activities would indicate that a male's daily caloric intake would increase from a daily basal level of 12 calories per pound of body weight to an

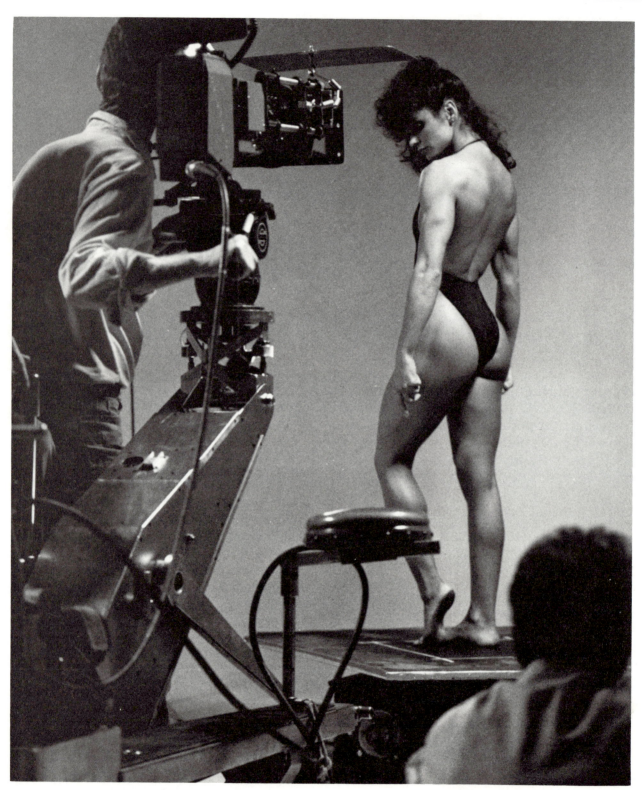

Gladys Portugues during the filming of one of her many television commercials.

average of 15–17 (even more in some cases) calories per pound, while the female increases from her basal level of 11 calories per pound to 12–14 calories per pound.

In your quest for a more accurate assessment of your estimated total energy expenditure, you might want to refer to these three excellent references:

G. Benard W. *CB/M Calories Burned per Minute.* CIS, Inc, 1984 edition.

This handy hardbound 160-page book lists over 1,000 food items, cross-referenced with over 75 lifestyle activities, according to weight classification. It is a must for serious bodybuilders who wish to estimate their energy requirements on a day-to-day basis. (Contact CIS, Inc., at 5415 Estates Dr., Oakland, CA 94618.)

Miller, A. T., and Morehouse, L. E. *Physiology of Exercise.* St. Louis: C. V. Mosby Company, 1976.

Sharkey, B. J. *Physiology and Physical Activity.* New York: Harper and Row, 1975.

MUSCLE MEASUREMENT CHART FOR MEN

Figures for determining IDEAL measurements for the average trainee

Biceps—2.10-inches
Multiply this figure by your wrist size.

Chest—5.62-inches
Multiply this figure by your wrist size.

Waist should equal
64% of chest girth.

Thighs—1.44-inches
Multiply this figure by knee measurement.

Calves should be
67% of thigh girth.

Body weight—2.55
Multiply this figure by height in inches.

Figures for determining HERCULEAN measurements for the serious bodybuilder

Biceps—2.32-inches
Multiply this figure by your wrist size.

Chest—6.42-inches
Multiply this figure by your wrist size.

Waist should equal
71% of chest girth.

Thighs—1.63-inches
Multiply this figure by knee measurement.

Calves should be
72% of thigh girth.

Body weight—3.1
Multiply this figure by height in inches.

Measure knees at smallest area.
Measure ankles around smallest part.
Measure wrist at smallest part.

Chart courtesy of John C. Grimek.

MEASUREMENT CHART FOR WOMEN

HEIGHT	BODY WEIGHT (POUNDS)	BUST	WAIST	HIPS	THIGHS
4'10"	90 95 100	31 to 34	21 to 22	31 to 34	17 to 19
4'11"	95 100 103	31 to 35	22 to 23	31 to 35	18 to 19
5'0"	100 107 112	32 to 35	23 to 25	32 to 35	18 to 20
5'1"	105 109 114	32 to 36	23 to 25	32 to 36	18 to 21
5'2"	106 111 117	33 to 36	24 to 26	32 to 36	19 to 21
5'3"	109 115 120	34 to 36	24 to 26	34 to 36	19 to 22
5'4"	112 116 122	35 to 37	24 to 27	35 to 37	19 to 22
5'5"	116 120 125	35 to 37	24 to 27	35 to 37	20 to 22
5'6"	120 125 130	36 to 38	24 to 28	36 to 38	20 to 23
5'7"	125 130 135	36 to 38	25 to 28	36 to 38	21 to 23
5'8"	130 138 143	37 to 39	25 to 29	37 to 39	22 to 24
5'9"	135 142 148	38 to 42	26 to 30	37 to 42	22 to 24

WRIST	ANKLE	CALF
5 to 7	7 to 9	11 to 15

The wrist, ankle, and calf measurements are for all women, regardless of their bone structures.

The low numbers on the WOMEN'S MEASUREMENT CHART are for those who are of a PETITE bone structure, while the middle and high numbers represent those women who have MEDIUM and LARGE bone structures respectively.

Mighty Mike Christian compares biceps with John Terilli.

World Champions Tina Plakinger and Tony Pearson.

13
SOME FACTS ABOUT BODY FAT

One characteristic that all individuals inherit is that of the accumulation of body fat cells. The normal fat cell is approximately 1/500 of an inch in diameter and can increase in number (fat cell hyperplasia) and size (fat cell hypertrophy).

The majority of fat cells are acquired during three distinct developmental stages in your life:

- Three months prior to birth
- One year after birth
- The teen years

Once you inherit your quota of body fat cells, that's it; only through a controlled diet and certain selected exercise regimens can fat cells be reduced in size. However, they can *never* be reduced in number, except by surgery.

Through some rather extensive clinical and laboratory research it has been determined that the average person (and this includes athletes) may acquire 25–30 billion fat cells, while the slightly obese person may acquire 50 billion fat cells, and the chronically obese individual can expect to amass an astounding 250 billion fat cells in his or her lifetime.

Judging from these laboratory findings, it is quite evident that chronically obese people who have done all they can to reduce their body weight to an acceptable limit will always have five times more chance of gaining back unwanted body fat than the slightly obese and eight times that of the average person.

Through continued exhaustive laboratory research, exercise physiologists have become extremely accurate at determining body fat percentages. This has been accomplished through a variety of testing measures such as the use of skin calipers, X-ray techniques, hydrostatic weighing (this shows you the difference in your body weight when compared to an equal volume of water).

The following guidelines are universally agreed on as the standard against which all men and women are compared regarding body fat percentages.

BODY FAT PERCENTAGES		MALE AND FEMALE	
1-10	Athlete	x	
10-14	Athlete		x
10-14	Average	x	
14-18	Average		x
20-22	Slightly Obese	x	
25-28	Slightly Obese		x
28-30	Chronically Obese	x	
35-38	Chronically Obese		x

There are a couple of mathematically derived formulas for determining body fat percentage that require only a measuring tape and a scale for weighing yourself. A pocket calculator would also be of some benefit to you in computing the necessary figures quickly.

Percentage Formula for Men

Subject: Weighs 190 pounds and has a 30-inch waist

The Numbers: 1.082/4.14/98.4 (lean body weight)

1.082 × 190 pounds (total body weight) = 205.6

4.14 × 30 (waist) = 124.2

Add: 98.4 (lean body weight) and 205.6 pounds (total body weight) = 304

Subtract: 124.2 from 304 = 179.8 (lean body weight)

Subtract: 179.8 (lean body weight) from 190 (total body weight) = 10.2 pounds

Fat Weight: 10.2 pounds

To determine the percentage of existing body fat:

Divide: The 10.2 pounds of fat weight by the total body weight of 190 pounds = 0.054

Multiply: 0.054 × 100 = 5.4 percent body fat

From this formula we can see that the above subject has a very low percentage of body fat for a male athlete.

Corinna Everson—two-time Ms. Olympia.

Percentage Formula
for Women

+8.987 = lean body weight
+0.732 *multiplied* by your body weight in kilograms
+3.768 *multiplied* by your wrist diameter in centimeters
−0.157 *multiplied* by your abdominal circumference in centimeters
−0.249 *multiplied* by your hip circumference in centimeters
+0.434 *multiplied* by your forearm circumference in centimeters

The following steps in the formula must be performed in the exact order in which they are listed.

First add the lean body weight figure to the two multiplied answers that have a plus symbol (+). You take this total and subtract from it the two (abdominal and hip) multiplied answers that have a minus symbol (−). You then take this answer and add it to the final (forearm) answer, and you will come up with a figure that represents your lean body weight in kilograms. The difference between your total body weight and your lean body weight in kilograms is your fat weight in kilograms. Convert your kilograms of TBW and LBW and fat weight into pounds by using the following formula:

Simply multiply a kilogram weight by 2. Example: 100 kilos × 2 = 200. Now take 10 percent of 200 = 20. Now add the two totals, and you will arrive at an answer of 220 pounds. To determine the percentage of existing body fat, follow the division method in the formula for men.

FAT-REDUCING METHODS

Body fat is stored throughout the entire body on all individuals, but it is not dis-

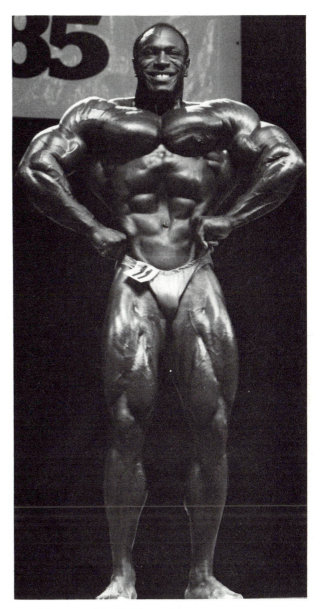

Lee Haney—Multi Olympian.

tributed in the same proportion for every person. Some people accumulate noticeable fat on their legs, particularly the inner thighs, while others have measurably more fat stored on their lower back, hips, waist, and buttocks. Generally speaking, though, a great many people tend to store a large percentage of fatty tissue around the waist. In an effort to

They sizzle! Couples champs Diana Dennis and Kevin Lawrence.

reduce body fat percentages, many people blindly adopt various methods or gimmicks that guarantee instant fat loss, but do they work?

The following is a partial list of the methods and items used in an attempt to reduce body fat:

Spot Reducing

This method calls for performing large numbers of sit-ups and leg raises in an attempt to reduce body fat from the waist. This method just doesn't work because fat is mobilized from throughout the body as a whole. Even if you could spot-reduce the waist, you wouldn't really burn up a lot of fat because the exercises involved are moving such a small muscle that it doesn't burn much fat.

Motorized Exercycles and Vibrating Belts

These are two of the more useless tools in existence for exercising. Neither one of these units challenges muscle cell activity in the body, and it is a fact that cell activity must be present in order to burn energy.

Neoprene Sauna Suits

Many individuals are under the impression that these suits are of some benefit in sweating off fat. This is simply not true. The only thing you might lose is some excess water weight, through the dehydration process, but that will be replaced when you quench your thirst. None of this water loss will come from the body fat, because body fat contains only a small percentage of water, 22 percent per pound of fat to be exact. There is some therapeutic value to the neoprene waist shaper or heat belt in that it does give a measure of support and keeps the lower back warm,

Carla Temple of Canada.

221

Unbelievable! Mike Christian squeezes into a "most muscular" pose.

which helps prevent injury, especially when performing overhead presses, hyperextensions, squatting exercises, deadlifts, and bent-over rowing movements.

Sauna Wraps

A few years ago, this was a very popular tool for losing inches *fast*. The procedure went something like this: you would be wrapped mummy-style with a clothlike wrap that had been soaked in a special chemical solution. You would then be transferred to a sauna, where you were to sit for a specified length of time. Upon completion of this phase, you would then be unwrapped and some rather hurried measurements would be taken. The inches lost were indeed evident, but if you were to have measurements taken again a few hours later without another wrapping procedure, the results once again would be startling, because they would be almost the same as prior to the sauna wrap procedure.

Most of the inches were lost due to the dehydration factor, and the arterial surface blood supply was forced deep into the inner body due to the wrapping procedures. Any wrapping procedures of this nature should be avoided. The only permanent losses will be from your pocketbook.

Electric Shock Machines

One of the claims of these units is that they will assist in burning body fat. The stimuli to a muscle area from one of these machines are so subtle that very little energy is used, and as a result reductions in body fat (*if any*) are just not that noticeable.

Exercise Body Creams

The manufacturers of these creams make borderline claims that, by applying this substance to your body and then exercising regularly and vigorously, you will burn body fat. The fact is that any body fat that is burned up as energy will be burned up as a result of a specific style of exercise and diet and not from a special exercise cream.

Up to this point we have drawn a very negative picture of the popular methods and gimmicks that many individuals use in an attempt to reduce body fat. There is, however, a foolproof method, which complements proper dieting, for reducing body fat. It is the champions' secret, and you can read about it in Chapter 9. "The Champions' Secret—Aerobics."

Muscular Laura Beaudry shows impressive glutes and legs.

14
A GUIDE TO LOSING EXCESS BODY WEIGHT

Many people are overweight because they take in many more calories than they need for their daily energy requirements. Simply stated, this is the classic case of overeating.

Some recent research done at Penn State University, published in the *Journal of the American Dietetic Association*, supports the theory that many people are poor judges of their own food intake. For example, nutritionists consider eight ounces of milk an average serving, but 66 percent of a test group took either a 6-ounce or a 10-ounce serving. Selecting orange juice, 50 percent of the group chose more than double the standard 4-ounce serving. In other random tests, many individuals neglected to report adding salad dressing (150 calories per ounce) to their salads. This habit alone, if done every day, could account for a gain of 15 pounds of body fat in a year's time. The obvious method for losing fat, therefore, is simply to eat fewer overall calories.

You can't count on the eyeball or "guestimate" method; you must weigh and measure your daily food. Two tools that will prove most helpful in this area are a food gram scale and an extensive book that lists food values of commonly used portions. This book should list the complete nutrient content of the foods: calories, cholesterol, sodium, fat, and much more.

During the first 10 days on a weight loss plan, the initial loss can be very unpredictable, because there is a shift in the water balance within the body along with the body fat loss. Water weighs more than the fat lost, and if it is retained it can show up as a gain in body weight.

Rules for Dieting

The following are 21 basic rules for successfully losing excess body weight in the form of body fat.

Tim Belknap—Mr. America and Mr. Universe.

1. Heavy, progressive-resistance exercise protects muscle tissue when dieting. If you diet without an exercise program to complement it, you can expect 65 percent of your weight loss to be muscle tissue and the remaining 35 percent body fat.

2. Avoid fasting and starvation diets. These are not recommended because even as little as 24 hours without food will excite the body to burn muscle tissue as energy while producing more fat enzymes, which in turn stores more fat. Similarly, avoid diets characterized by limitations on certain nutrients in favor of others, such as high-protein/no-carb diets and high-carb/no-protein schemes. You may experience very rapid weight losses on these radical diets, but only at the expense of good health.

3. Don't skip meals. Eat on a regular time schedule whenever possible

4. Spread out your caloric intake throughout the day. If you must eat only one well-balanced meal a day, be sure that it is eaten in the morning rather than in the evening. (See rule no. 16.)

5. Avoid concentrated calories, which stimulate your appetite and cause you to overeat. Many of these types of foods are listed in the table entitled "Foods to Avoid," found in Chapter 11, "The Nutrient Factor."

6. You will burn more calories by exercising the day after overeating (Thanksgiving Day, for example) than after a day of normal eating. Don't overeat more than two days in a row!

7. Cut back on junk foods gradually rather than with a dramatic all-at-once effort. Trick the body.

8. Exercising before eating a main meal will in some cases depress the appetite, and as a result you are less likely to overeat.

9. Never put more food on your plate than you need to meet the particular meal calorie quota.

10. Cut or divide your sandwiches, fresh fruits, and vegetables into segments (cut an apple into quarters, e.g.). This will give you the feeling of eating more though you are not.

11. If there is a particular food that you enjoy that may set you off on an eating binge, eliminate it completely from your nutritional plan.

12. Prepare all your meals and snacks ahead of time. It is easier to control your caloric needs this way.

13. The pace at which you eat is an important principle of dieting. Eat your foods *slowly* so that the stomach will be able to signal the brain when you have had enough food.

14. Eating consistently is important when you are on a weight loss plan, but so is an occasional splurge (like a massive Thanksgiving Day dinner) to relieve your mind of the feeling of self-denial.

15. Many authorities on diet control suggest that you should not partake of second helpings at mealtime. However, you *can* trick yourself into feeling you've indulged by making your first serving only half the required calories for that particular meal, but only if you plan to eat a second helping.

16. Don't eat after 8:00 P.M. The metabolism slows down by approximately 8–10 percent during this time period and through your sleeping hours. Therefore, eating after 8:00 means there is a good possibility that you might gain excess body fat. Speaking of metabolism, age is a factor that determines its efficiency. Your metabolism becomes less efficient after the age of 20. Lean muscle tissue begins to decrease while existing fat cells increase in size. This factor is more evident in persons who do not participate in some form of exercise. To compensate for this problem, simply reduce your daily caloric intake by 2 percent for every 10-year period past the age of 20. For example, at age 30 your daily caloric intake may be a hypothetical 3,000 calories per day. Two percent less than 3,000 calories would be 2,940 calories. At age 40 you would reduce

your caloric intake by 4 percent, for a total of 2,822. At age 50, you would deduct 6 percent from your caloric expenditure of 2,822 calories, and this figures out to be 2,663 calories per day for the next 10

Moses Moldanado.

227

years. Remember that caloric expenditure is dependent on such conditions as existing body weight, training intensity, rate of breathing, age, and metabolic changes in the body.

17. Make sure that you are taking in plenty of calcium each day. If you become deficient in this mineral, you may acquire a degree of nervousness, and this in turn can cause you to overeat.

18. Speed up your metabolic rate and burn more calories by starting on an aerobic conditioning plan.

19. As we've mentioned, the first 10 days of a weight loss plan are very unpredictable. After this time period you can expect to lose approximately 4 ounces of body fat per day, or 1¾–2 pounds per week. Generally, losses beyond this average might prove to be water and muscle tissue.

The exception: Losing 4 ounces of body fat per day might prove to be too drastic a change for the fit bodybuilder whose body fat percentage is in the range of 10–14 percent for the male and 14–18 percent for the female. For those of you who are in this select category, your body fat losses should not amount to more than 1 pound per week.

20. Reducing your daily quota of calories is important in the body fat weight loss plan. This can be accomplished by reducing your daily caloric intake by 250–500 to as much as 1,000 calories, seven days per week and for as many weeks as necessary to achieve your goal of body fat weight loss. A pound of fat is equal to 3,500 calories.

*Reduce Daily Caloric
Intake by*
250 calories
500 calories
1,000 calories

Lee Labrada, winner of the 1986 "Night of Champions" shows the ultimate in muscularity and symmetry.

*Reduce Pounds
of Body Fat by*
½ pound per week
1 pound per week
2 pounds per week

For the nonathlete who is using a daily caloric ratio of 50 percent complex carbohydrates, 17.5 percent complete proteins, and 32.5 percent unsaturated fats, daily caloric reduction should come mainly from fat sources. However, your daily fat sources should never be completely eliminated. Always include approximately 15 grams (135 calories) of unsaturated fats in your daily diet whatever diet scheme you follow.

If you're a sports athlete or body-builder who is using an optimum ratio of 65 percent complex carbohydrates, 25 percent complete proteins, and 10 percent unsaturated fats, you should reduce your daily caloric percentages of the three listed nutrients evenly.

A nutrition tip worth remembering is always to be sure that, for every 100 calories you eat, 20 of those are in the form of a complex carbohydrate This will help you prevent a state of ketosis.

21. Regardless of the reducing plan you decide to use, your daily calorie levels should never drop below these figures:
men, 1,400 calories
women, 1,100 calories.

Dieting Secret

Remember that the dietary control method for losing excess body weight in the form of body fat requires patience and perseverance. Always set your daily, monthly, and long-term goals in a manner that you can live with. Take small steps to reach these goals rather than attempting to make major changes all at once.

California's Steve Davis.

15
OVERCOMING WATER RETENTION

One major problem common among body-builders is the inability to control water retention. You can safely drop 3–4 percent of water weight without experiencing *any* negative effects on your existing strength levels. Any further losses can and will in some cases result in an approximate 1½-pound loss from each major lifting exercise for each pound of body weight lost. For example, if you lose 3 pounds of body weight beyond the maximums cited above, expect in most cases to lose 4½ pounds off your lifting poundage.

Here are some techniques you can use to prevent water retention:

1. Limit your salt intake. Beware of foods that contain salt! A sodium level book can tell you how much sodium is in various foods. This is very important because one part sodium retains 180 parts water. The normal sodium requirement for an adult is 200 mg per day, though the average American takes in 5,000–10,000 mg per day.

Salt intake abuse happens in a very discreet manner. A single Big Mac from McDonald's, for example, contains approximately 1,000 mg of salt. It doesn't take too much math to figure out that you exceed the normal daily requirement for salt with just one or two hearty bites from the Big Mac and are well on your way to the average 5,000–10,000 mg by eating other sodium-containing foods. To prevent too much sodium from sneaking into your diet, use your sodium level book and also refer to the "Foods to Avoid" table in Chapter 11.

2. Reduce your daily water intake by 60 percent. For example, if you weigh 160 pounds and normally drink 80 ounces of liquid daily (or 10 8-ounce glasses), you will cut back to 4 8-ounce glasses. If you have problems with quenching your thirst, try sucking on fresh lemons throughout the day, but only if you don't have any gastric problems.

3. Stay away from the carbohydrate-

Canada's Deanna Panting with Mary Roberts from the U.S.

loading plan during this week if you have a problem with water retention from an overconsumption of carbs.

4. Induced sweating will help release water from between the outer layer of skin and the muscle tissue. One thing that will promote sweating, if used regularly during your workouts, is a neoprene sauna suit. Some individuals find that these sauna suits irritate the skin when used alone or next to the skin surface. If you find this to be true, put on a lightweight cotton (absorbs water best) warm-up suit first. Now put the neoprene suit on over that. Be sure that both suits are large enough to allow for maximum mobility in your workouts. You might also use these suits on your scheduled jogging days.

Rocky DeFerro achieves his mass partly through a muscle-building diet.

16
TEN TIPS FOR GAINING MUSCULAR BODY WEIGHT

1. To gain a pound of muscle per week you need to do several high-intensity workouts *and* increase your daily food consumption by 100–200 calories per day. The reason you don't do the opposite of the weight loss procedure described earlier (eating 500 fewer calories a day to lose a pound of fat per week) is that here you want to gain weight in the form of *muscle*, not fat, and muscle and fat differ in water, protein, and fat content.

This chemical breakdown shows that our skeletal muscle weight is made up of almost three-quarters water. We now know that muscle and fat are two diverse substances that differ considerably in composition. This leads us to the subject of muscles turning to fat, a common myth.

It simply isn't true that muscles can turn into fat, but it's not hard to understand how this misconception arises. A football player at the peak of his career, for example, is playing the game with great intensity and regularity each week. He is also working out hard with weights. He is consuming a tremendous number of calories each day to sustain this energy output. Now look what happens when he retires. He is no longer playing football, so his energy requirements are noticeably lower. While he may continue to work out with weights, over a period of months this activity usually ceases completely, and as a result his energy requirements are dramatically reduced. But at the same time, the football player is consuming the same number of calories per day as when he was playing football and working out with weights. Basically, this is what happens: lack of physical activity such as playing football and pumping iron has caused the muscles to atrophy or diminish in cell size. Consuming more calories than he needs contributes to some rather large gains in body fat. Some of this body fat forms a layer between the skin and the muscle cell (which has diminished in size

POUND OF	WATER	PROTEIN	FAT	CALORIES
Muscle	70%	22%	8%	600
Fat	22%	6%	72%	3,500

from lack of exercise stimuli), and this gives the illusion of muscle turning to fat. If this person had a proper knowledge of nutrition and exercise, he would have decreased his caloric intake in accordance with his marked decrease in physical activity. Had he also continued with some type of workouts, whether aerobics or circuit weight training, he would have been able to maintain stimulus to his muscles while preventing fat gain by reducing his caloric intake. This example disproves the myth that muscle turns to fat, but it also shows what can happen to an athlete in any sport who does not eat right or train smart.

Eating to gain requires that you figure out your daily menu for each day of the week. Eat basically the same foods from each of the food groups as you normally would. If you do make a substitute (for sanity's sake), be sure the replacement is of the same caloric value. In this way you won't constantly have to refer to a calorie book.

2. Slow down your basal metabolic rate by doing absolutely nothing beyond your daily obligations such as family, job, and workouts. Don't participate in any extra sports activities, whether bowling, hockey, golf, marathon running, racquet sports, soccer, softball, tennis, volleyball, or wrestling.

3. Try to get eight to nine hours of sleep each night. We are speaking of quality sleep, where you retire an hour or so before midnight and sleep through until 7:00 A.M. or so. If at all possible, try to take a short one-hour nap during the afternoon. Those of you who are working at a

Rich Gaspari shows what he's got!

job requiring a swing or graveyard shift will have to adjust your sleeping hours accordingly.

4. Don't stand when you can sit, walk when you can ride, etc.

5. Don't smoke, because this constricts the blood capillary beds in the

body, which in turn has a debilitating effect on oxygen-carrying enzymes in the body. Smoking also triggers a rise in blood sugar levels, which depresses your appetite. Now you can begin to understand why smokers who quit gain weight rapidly (which is not to say that those who are overweight should start smoking as a means of depressing the appetite to lose weight). Smoking also destroys vitamin C at the rate of 35 milligrams (one orange) per cigarette.

Sergio Oliva at the 1985 Mr. Olympia contest.

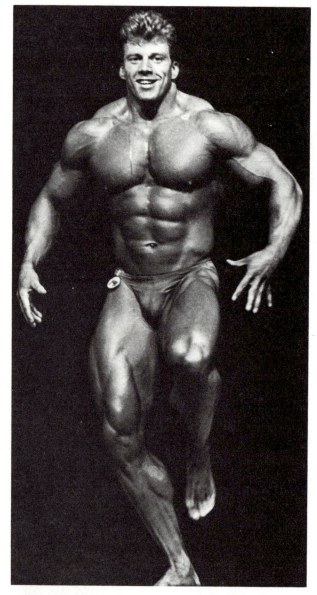

Matt Mendenhall having fun on stage.

oping a physical ease and a positive energy source.

8. Never allow yourself to get hungry. To prevent hunger, try eating four or five times per day, perhaps three substantial main meals with three smaller feedings or snacks in between. This meal schedule will allow you the best utilization and assimilation of your foods.

9. Be sure to include digestive enzyme tablets (pineapple enzymes) at each meal or snack to aid digestive efficiency.

10. After very diligently following the advice given in secrets 1–9, some of you

Wow! The greatest legs to walk out on stage.

6. Do *not* exercise directly before a meal since that may depress your appetite.

7. Avoid those uptight situations that upset the nervous system and burn up valuable calories. To do so you must know yourself and how to react to people. Eliminate anger, anxiety, fear, frustration, and the like whenever possible. Work at devel-

SEVEN-WEEK CALORIE CYCLE

Current Body Weight: 180 Pounds   **Daily Calories Consumed: 3,440**

WEEK NO.	EXTRA CALORIES PER DAY	DAILY CALORIES CONSUMED
1	2 × body weight = 360	3,800
2	3 × body weight = 540	3,980
3	4 × body weight = 720	4,160
4	5 × body weight = 900	4,340
5	6 × body weight = 1,080	4,520
6	7 × body weight = 1,260	4,700
7	8 × body weight = 1,440	4,880

The above approximations are for a moderately active bodybuilder in his twenties and are based on the information supplied in Chapter 12,"Estimating Your Energy Expenditure." Both men and women can use this blitz method of gaining weight, though we feel that these extremes are not necessary for 99 percent of women. Secret No. 1 will prove adequate for most women athletes.

The 7-week blitz gaining cycle can be expanded to a 14-week cycle in which you add one calorie every two weeks as opposed to every week.

Also, you may begin to notice weight gains before the 7 or 14 weeks are up. If this is the case, after you have reached your desired additional body weight using this system, gradually drop back off this blitz calorie intake to a maintenance calorie level that will maintain your new body weight.

---

may find that gains in muscular body weight are still not apparent. If you suspect that the problem may be due to your daily caloric consumption, try the unique *blitz method* described below for gaining that extra muscular body weight you desire.

THE UNIQUE BLITZ METHOD

To explain this procedure, here is a hypothetical example: you are a 180-pound bodybuilder who is moderately active, and your daily estimated energy expenditure is 3,440 calories. In order to gain additional muscular body weight, include *two extra* calories per pound of your existing body weight per day. If you are still not making any progress, then each week for the next six weeks you should add *one extra* calorie per pound of body weight, up to a maximum (for both men and women) of eight calories.

Massive Bertil Fox.

239

The magnificent chest of superstar Rich Gaspari.

The incredible back of Juliette Bergman.

The above approximations are for a moderately active bodybuilder in his twenties and are based on the information supplied in Chapter 12, "Estimating Your Energy Expenditure." Both men and women can use this blitz method of gaining weight, though we feel that these extremes are not necessary for 99 percent of women. Secret No. 1 will prove adequate for most women athletes.

The 7-week blitz gaining cycle can be expanded to a 14-week cycle in which you add one calorie every two weeks as opposed to every week.

Also, you may begin to notice weight gains before the 7 or 14 weeks are up. If this is the case, after you have reached your desired additional body weight using this system, gradually drop back off this blitz calorie intake to a maintenance calorie level that will maintain your new body weight.

Gaining additional body weight in the manner described requires that you eat a lot of food. Those of you who simply can't get along with this requirement might try mixing up one of the blender drinks listed in Chapter 18 and consider this part of your daily calorie consumption. You can even carry this one step further by setting your alarm clock for an early morning rising, say around 2:00 A.M. or so, have a protein drink at this time, and then get back to sleep as quickly as possible.

Protein tablets are a good item to carry with you on the job or at school when you can't eat a normal meal.

Another method that has proven to be beneficial in the promotion of muscular weight gains is to eat 1 boiled egg every hour that you are awake.

SIGNS OF GAINING WEIGHT TOO QUICKLY

A need for more sleep than usual, shortness of breath, lack of energy, and excessive sweating are all signs that you've gained muscle weight too quickly. Many bodybuilding authorities say that you generally can't gain more than 10–12 pounds of muscle body weight in 12 months. This is generally true for advanced bodybuilders, especially seasoned competitors. (Be assured that a beginner or an intermediate bodybuilder may realize some rather exceptional gains in muscular body weight beyond those mentioned.)

TOOLS

Some tools that you will find helpful in your quest for gaining muscular body weight or losing excess body fat are a measuring tape, a mirror, and an accurate bathroom scale. If you are in the process of losing weight, it is always a good idea to weigh yourself in the morning after rising because you are at your lightest in the early morning hours and at your heaviest during the evening around 8:00 P.M. Those of you in the gaining process can reverse this procedure and weigh yourselves in the evening, prior to retiring.

One of the world's best proportioned yet muscular physiques belongs to Serge Nubret.

17
CARBOHYDRATE LOADING

The carbohydrate-loading technique was developed by a Swedish exercise physiologist, Eric Hultman, as a means by which athletes could store more carbohydrates (glycogen) in the muscle tissue than normal. It has been determined through research that carbohydrate, in the form of glycogen, is stored in the muscle at 1.75 grams per 100 grams of muscle. After the first three days of the depletion phase of the carbohydrate-loading technique, the glycogen levels in the body drop down to approximately ½ gram per 100 grams of muscle. The best part comes upon completion of the three-day carbing-up phase. Glycogen capacities in the muscle have now increased to as much as 3–5 grams per 100 grams of muscle. This is a marked increase of 70–185 percent above normal. This means that athletes will have a glucose/glycogen saturation for their chosen athletic event, be it a marathon or some other endurance sport.

HOW CARBOHYDRATE LOADING WORKS

Begin the carbohydrate-loading technique six days prior to the event.

The Depletion Phase: Days 1, 2, and 3

Depletion of the carbohydrates stored in the muscle is efficiently accomplished by high-intensity/high-volume exercise activity and carefully controlled nutrition.

You can choose from many training routines to accomplish carbohydrate depletion. If you're training in the off-season and desire to participate in an endurance sport, you might perform high-volume training, 10–12 sets per muscle group, 8–15 reps per set, and 4–5 sets per exercise. If you're a powerlifter, you may decide to use training loads of 84–88 percent of 1-

rep maximum for numerous sets of 6–8 reps in the 3 powerlifts and some additional assistance exercises, using 80 percent of a 1-rep maximum in the chosen exercise for a few sets of 12–14 repetitions.

Basically, you will want to perform workouts that will burn up glycogen as energy substrate at a rate of 10–20 calories per minute over a daily 2-hour time period. Each major body part should be worked for approximately 45 minutes. The key to assuring yourself of total carbohy-drate depletion is to work each body part as hard and fast as possible. Therefore, you will not work all the body parts in one workout but will find it of more benefit to use a split routine in which you work one or two body parts to the absolute maximum.

On the next two days (2 and 3), your workouts should be light to moderate in intensity due to the depletion in existing strength levels.

Controlled eating is very important to the success of both the depletion and

Negrita Jayde works her chest.

Bob Birdsong—Mr. America.

carbing-up phases of carbohydrate loading. During the three-day depletion phase, you should eat a very high-protein diet. In other words, eliminate most of your carbohydrate sources except for 50 grams (200 calories) daily, which is vital for proper brain functioning. The brain demands 50 or so grams of glucose per day, and this is quite in line with the conversion of carbohydrate (glycogen), which converts to blood glucose at a rate of 2 grams (8 calories) per hour. Your selection of foods should come from complete proteins, which contain no saturated fats.

It is interesting to note that for every gram of glycogen you burn up, three grams of water accompany it. More than likely you will notice a drop in your existing body weight, but be assured that it is probably water weight. You should schedule five to six feedings per day, and these feedings should be three to four hours apart.

A note on the 50-grams-per-day carbohydrate requirement is necessary. Rather than eating all your carbohydrates (50 grams) at one meal, it is better to eat 25 grams with an early morning protein feeding and the remaining 25 grams during a late afternoon or evening protein meal.

Carbohydrate or glycogen depletion in the muscle can't really be monitored accurately. You can only hope that a regimen of hard and fast training will accomplish it. However, you *can* monitor the blood glucose by using chemically treated papers called *keto sticks*. These papers are dipped or placed in a urine sample you have taken; the deeper the shade of purple, the less glucose you have in your blood.

The Carbing-Up Phase: Days 4, 5, and 6

During these last three days of the carbohydrate-loading technique, all exercise activity should cease to allow maximal carbohydrate saturation within the muscle cells. An important point to remember here is that you will have to decrease your daily caloric intake because your energy requirements are now lower due to the termination of the workout sessions.

Take in only enough calories to meet your estimated daily caloric expenditure. You are not interested in gaining muscle weight or losing body fat, but rather in maintaining your current body weight. The opposite of what you experienced in the depletion phase regarding fluctuations in body weight will occur during

John Kemper shows an impressive side chest.

this phase: you may find yourself a few pounds heavier. This is generally the result of a water retention problem stemming from the massive amounts of carbohydrates you've consumed (with three parts water attaching to one part carbohydrate). This problem will alleviate itself after the scheduled athletic event.

During these three days, eat loads of complex carbohydrates along with some complete proteins and unsaturated fats. Your daily ratio of these nutrients should be as follows: carbs, 70 percent; proteins, 25 percent; fats, 5 percent.

Note that there are some differences between how a man should approach the carbing-up phase and how a woman should do so. Some women can totally carb up in a 24-hour period, whereas a 200-pound man will need all 3 days, or 72 hours, in which to accomplish this critical phase of carbohydrate loading. With this in mind, it would be a good idea to practice the carbohydrate-loading technique once or twice during the year just to see how your body reacts to it, rather than trying it for the very first time before an important athletic event and experiencing some disappointments.

Another noted difference in the approach to carbing up for men and women has to do with simple sugars. When a man takes in 20 percent or more of his daily calories in the form of simple sugars, the liver immediately converts the simple sugars to triglycerides or fat. This does not generally happen in women. Testosterone levels are responsible in part for this. The normal male produces 2.5–10 mg a day, while a woman produces only 0.23 mg. This fact alone should make it clear why a woman can't develop large muscle mass under normal conditions.

Eat simple (but only in the percentages listed earlier in this chapter) and complex carbs. Avoid those carbs that are super-high in fiber. Moderation is the key here. Avoid fats except for the daily allowable percentage. Load up on apples, melons, strawberries, whole wheat pancakes, pasta, potatoes, rice, grains, waffles, etc.

Spread your meals out as mentioned for the depletion phase. This is carbohydrate loading at its optimum. For several reasons, you should not attempt carb loading more than three to four times a year:

1. During the first three days there is a loss of fiber content due to the lack of fibrous complex carbohydrates, which in turn causes diarrhea to occur occasionally.

2. During the depletion phase of carbohydrate loading, there are some radical changes in ratio quotas of the carbs and proteins, and this has a diuretic effect (promoting the discharge of urine) on the body. As a result, your body becomes deficient in mineral potassium.

3. There is a slight increase in the triglycerides (fat) stored in the body due to the rather sudden loss of carbohydrate stores, which are in part necessary for intercellular fat metabolizing.

4. When not enough carbohydrate (glycogen) is stored in the muscles and liver, protein from the muscle is converted to an energy source. In order to convert the protein into an energy source, the nitrogen is stripped from the protein molecules. The remaining carbon and oxygen molecules combine to create an energy source much like that of the carbohydrate.

The problem arises with the excess nitrogen previously stripped from the protein molecules. The isolated nitrogen molecules form a toxic ammonia compound, which is rejected by the liver into the bloodstream. This rather toxic compound travels through the bloodstream

Mike Christian—the human mountain.

and eventually is filtered through the kidneys. The end result, of course, is an overworked liver and kidney, and this is simply not healthy when carried to an extreme.

The Day of the Athletic Event

1. Don't miss a scheduled meal on this day. Keep in mind that four to five hours should elapse between your final meal and the scheduled competition. This will allow for maximum digestion of the foods.
2. Avoid overeating or excess calorie consumption during these meals. Eat only enough to stave off that precompetition feeling of general weakness.
3. Eat only complex carbohydrates, and these should be of the lowest fiber content.
4. No protein or fat sources are allowed on this day, and this includes a time frame of 12 hours prior to the scheduled event.

POWERLIFTERS BEWARE

This type of diet is not recommended for powerlifters. It works quite adequately for those in endurance sports but not for powerlifters. This diet would present a problem in any sport in which you are entering a certain weight division. For example, to lose 10 pounds you would have to begin five meals prior to the event; to lose 6–8 pounds, you would have to begin three meals prior; to lose 4 pounds, you would start two meals before; to lose 2 pounds you would begin the evening before. Obviously, when demands of this nature are required, effective carbohydrate-loading techniques are not always possible.

"The Ageless One" Al Beckles begins his routine at the 1985 Olympia contest.

18
BLENDER MAGIC

To add some variety to your daily nutritional regimen, you might find it refreshing to try one of the nutritional drinks below. These drinks can be used as a part of your body fat reduction program, where you substitute one of these drinks for a meal or snack. They can also be added to your daily diet to help you obtain those extra calories so necessary for gaining muscular body weight.

Blender drinks are a good way to get needed calories, but they contain a tremendous number of *concentrated* calories, so it is very easy to drink more calories than you would normally eat at a particular meal.

Blender drinks should never dominate a daily diet to the point of causing you to exceed your daily caloric needs. If, for example, you choose the Postworkout Drink to use as a meal replacement for the purpose of reducing, the calorie content may exceed your requirements for that particular meal. If this is the case, go ahead and utilize the drink as planned, but then eat less at your next meal in order to balance out your daily calorie quota.

Then again, you may find that some of these drinks have fewer calories than you need for a particular meal replacement. In this case, you could double the ingredients, and hopefully this would ensure that you receive adequate calories. Or you might use the drink in conjunction with some solid food selections.

To prepare each of the drinks below, simply whirl the ingredients in an electric blender until smooth. Each recipe makes one serving.

Note: all calorie counts are approximations.

The ever-popular Franco Columbu.

Banana Flip (426 calories)

1⅓ cups cold whole milk

1 medium banana

1 tablespoon raw honey

1 tablespoon milk and egg protein
 powder

1 cup crushed ice

Beatty Fruit Cocktail (240 calories)

Equal amounts apple juice, orange
 juice, and papaya juice to make 1⅓
 cups

5 frozen strawberries

1 cup crushed ice

Coconut Pro (440 calories)

⅔ cup apple juice
⅔ cup pineapple coconut juice
1 medium banana
5 frozen strawberries
1 cup crushed ice

Preworkout Drink
(520 calories)

Equal amounts orange juice, apple
    juice, and papaya juice to make 1⅓
    cups
1 tablespoon milk and egg protein
    powder
1 tablespoon Hoffman's Energol
1 tablespoon lecithin powder
1 tablespoon raw honey
1 medium banana
5 frozen strawberries
1 cup crushed ice

Smoothie (247 calories)

⅔ cup orange juice
⅔ cup papaya juice
½ medium banana
1 tablespoon honey
1 cup crushed ice

Hawaiian Delight
(225 calories)

⅔ cup papaya juice
⅔ cup pineapple coconut juice
1 medium banana
1 cup crushed ice

Orange Sunrise (430 calories)

1⅓ cups orange juice
2 large scoops natural vanilla ice cream

Marjo Selin from Finland—an upcoming star.

253

Piña Colada (228 calories)

1⅓ cups pineapple coconut juice
1 medium banana
1 tablespoon pure vanilla extract
1 cup crushed ice

Diet Delight (172 calories)

8 ounces papaya juice
1 tablespoon milk and egg protein
 powder
3 fresh or frozen strawberries

Two of the all-time greats, Frank Zane and Chris Dickerson.

Strawberry Fruit Flip
(297 calories)

1⅓ cups papaya juice
5 frozen strawberries
½ medium banana
1 tablespoon raw honey
1 cup crushed ice

Instant Energizer
(328 calories)

8 ounces natural fruit juice
1 egg
1 tablespoon milk and egg protein
    powder
½ banana
1 teapoon raw honey

Kwik Gain Drink
(658 calories)

8 ounces half-and-half
2 eggs
2 tablespoons milk and egg protein
    powder
½ banana
1 teaspoon honey
1 scoop natural ice cream

Postworkout Drink
(730 calories)

1 cup papaya juice
½ cup cold whole milk
1 tablespoon milk and egg protein
    powder
1 tablespoon lecithin powder
1 tablespoon Hoffman's Energol
1 tablespoon raw honey
1 medium banana
5 frozen strawberries
1 cup crushed ice
2 large scoops of natural ice cream

Mike Christian's unbelievable back.

Citrus Energy Drink
(650 calories)

1 whole orange
1 whole lemon
1 pint unsweetened pineapple juice
1,000 IU vitamin E (d-alpha)
2 tablespoons Hoffman's Energol
3 tablespoons malted milk powder
Raw honey

Grate off the outer oily rind of the citrus fruits until there is no color left and discard colored rind. Chop pulp, removing seeds, and blend the fruits with pineapple juice. Then mix in vitamin E, Hoffman's Energol, malted milk powder, and enough raw honey to make this drink taste decent.

Drink one-third of this drink three times per day.

Gorgeous Rachel McLish and Clare Furr start to pose.

19
THE FINAL COMMENT

Only with intelligence and a will to learn about your body can you realize maximum size, strength, and health. With this thought in mind, we conclude this book with 10 fundamental principles that will help you in your future bodybuilding training:

1. Strive to obtain a symmetrical and proportionate physique.
2. Squats are the most important single exercise for a beginner, intermediate, or advanced bodybuilder.
3. Learn all you possibly can from the various bodybuilding journals and numerous books and courses pertaining to the subject of bodybuilding.
4. Learn all you can about the subject of nutrition.
5. Talk to others who are devoted to the sport of bodybuilding.
6. Always stay alert to new ideas and developments in the bodybuilding field.
7. Believe in yourself and your ability to succeed in bodybuilding.
8. Never rate yourself in comparison to others. Be the very best *you* can be.
9. Strive to better past performances and goals!
10. Don't make an excuse to miss a workout. This is the cause of most bodybuilding failures.

Hopefully, the information we provided you with here will aid you in the pursuit of muscular magnificence. And remember, to achieve such muscularity it must be a holistic effort—mind, body, and spirit. Now go for it! We're behind you all the way.

INDEX